C000135018

FLOWER FACTORY

FLOWER FACTORY

A FAIRY TALE

Richard Foster

ORTAC PRESS

Copyright © Richard Foster 2022
All rights reserved.

The right of Richard Foster to be identified as the author
of this work has been asserted by him in accordance with
the Copyright, Designs and Patents Act 1988.

First published in Great Britain in 2022 by Ortac Press

ISBN: 978-1-8383887-1-3

A CIP record for this book is available from the British Library.

Cover design by Viktor Hachmang
Illustrations by the author
Set in Quadraat by Tetragon, London
Printed and bound in the UK by Xpedient Book Print

ortacpress.com

To my mother, father, brother and partner.

PLAY LOUD.

INTRODUCTION

THESE DAYS the notion of upping sticks and looking for work in another country seems to be reserved for the decadent or desperate. Not so long ago it was just one element of the broader pattern of British working life.

It's worth remembering that the Irish and the British have been working on the Continent for hundreds of years, building railways, cathedrals and factories, serving in armies and, since the recessions and economic readjustments of the 1970s and 1980s, trading apprenticeships and skills forged in the days of the white heat of technology for a pay packet to send home. By the 1980s the notion of 'working abroad' had entered the rhythms of British popular culture, if you take the popularity of TV's *Auf Wiedersehen, Pet* as proof.

Around that time the reasons to go overseas expanded to reflect younger and more diverse social groups. Talking of just the United Kingdom, new lives begun away from urban and rural poverty, civil unrest and the Troubles now encompassed ideas and incentives around gap years and playing at being New Age Warriors (for those who could just about afford it), squat and punk culture, drug habits in South East

Asia, keeping the beat alive or just a feeling that nothing was panning out. The latter was me.

The Netherlands was an easy destination to settle on. It was seen as a compact, friendly country, not too far away, where 'everyone' spoke English. There was also talk of a generous social-security system. In any case, work was easily available, well regulated and often not too onerous. Cycling was a boon, too, as everything (work, drugs and music) seemed accessible by bike. Employment in the bulb and plant sector also fed nascent hippy dreams of contributing to something 'peaceful', a way of living that, if not wholly off the land, was at least connected to Dame Nature's healing aura. The sector's seasonality also meant those who needed to get away from civilization could get their holiday stamps paid out and jet off to Goa, Thailand, Vietnam and sometimes South and Central America to sate their wanderlust or get even more wrecked, away from the bitter Dutch winters.

Looking back it's clear, to me at any rate, that by transmitting and receiving notions of individuality, personal rebellion and social justice, Amsterdam, the Magic Centre of the Universe, especially in its 1960s, 70s and 80s guise as a utopia of personal freedoms and intermediary for a nation, still sent out frazzled signals for many.

Unbeknownst to us, the country in the year 2000 was on the cusp of change. The euro, Schengen and a post-9/11 shift rightwards combined over the coming decade to usher in a new, more inward-looking era. Just talking of the city that, for many non-Dutch, so often stands in for the whole country, I think it's fair to say that the Amsterdam of *Koninginnedag* 2000 and that of 2019, let alone the post-COVID, post-Brexit bonanza, *uber*-clean Amsterdam to come, may as well exist on different continents.

It is twenty-one years since these events began to morph into memories. Some seem burned onto my retina, others appear out of the gloaming like a carp in a canal, tricked by the bait of other remembrances.

Because of that tricksiness, I thought long and hard about how best to set these memories down, finally allowing the baked, dazzled, flash-fried luminosity of their inner characters, and the deep-grained, ever-silent weirdness of the Netherlands, to do the running. I certainly didn't want to position it all as a social history or stake my claim as any kind of reliable narrator of the times and places I found myself in. My luck was to come in and see it all, stage left, as the whole scene was incrementally dismantled and then transported over the Lethe. So these flashbacks should be read as a series of fictions. All the characters' names are made up by me. Most stories are 'true' but are impossible to tell without the elements that aren't. Others have been warped into other spaces entirely, lost broadcasts fuzzily available on the astral plane.

But like my dreams of my old hometown, Accrington, where I often see the place as a vast wasteland of buildings made of decaying paper and rags, slowly decomposing under the magnificent Victorian railway arch, they must mean something. Yours to choose, and, oh yeah: take it easy!

Richard Foster, June 2021

SPRING

THE HOUSE OF DOUBTFUL MUSIC

THOSE FIRST IMPRESSIONS

SATURDAY, 1 APRIL 2000. I say goodbye to my perturbed parents at the Harwich ferry terminal, where I am taking the day crossing to the Hook of Holland. The previous day we drove down from Lancashire, put up at a B&B and ate a huge fish-and-chip supper in a local cafe, maybe as a way of armouring ourselves for the following day. The same impetus is probably behind the demolition of a cooked breakfast with every imaginable trimming on the morning of the sail. Filling ourselves up with memories. Mine to take with me as a final ritual ingestion of England; my parents' as two 'family moments' shared with their restless son.

The ferry crossing itself is fairly uneventful, and I notice hardly anything apart from the lads behind the bar, who are, to my way of thinking, the most Dutch-looking people I have ever seen: real-life versions of Frans Hals's guardians of the Haarlem Guild. Red-faced, moustachioed and stocky, comporting themselves with an easy swagger, they shout confirmations of my orders back as if we are in a musical. I get 'Take it easy!' thrown at me a few times. They must be taking the piss.

Once docked, and yanking two heavy rucksacks off the towpath, I get on the train going to the city of Leiden, where my scribbled notes tell me I will get a bus to the seaside town of Noordwijk, close to the campsite where I have booked a caravan for the whole summer. Once in Noordwijk I can work out how to get to my new home; surely it can't be too difficult. I take in very little of my journey at first, apart from pinching myself at the fact that I'm on a train in another country.

Pulling into Rotterdam Centraal, I stare out of the window at two hunched, middle-aged station guards. The men amble about in half-circles and do very little else, outside of leaning against the concrete wall of a waiting room once one of them has blown his whistle, signalling my train can depart. The station seems cavernous, and the daylight loses out to the solid concrete and metal surroundings. Everything feels transported from another time, maybe the 1950s. Augmenting this impression is the bony, lizard-like gentleman who sits opposite me after getting on at Rotterdam. Wearing a dark suit, polished black brogues and sunglasses, his black hair is greased back and follows the contours of his skull. His skin resembles crinkled brown paper. A huge cigar completes the picture, the smoke from which forms in clouds around his head. Another type of Dutchman to add to my collection of slow-moving guards and red-faced bartenders. Now and again he cackles and wheezes to himself in a voice that sounds like a creaking door. Without doubt he is a most cadaverous chap, and slightly unnerving to boot.

Getting off at Leiden Centraal, I make for the bus station plaza, a place I remember from a period as a sales rep a couple of years previously when I would sometimes attend trade fairs in the country. This familiarity, albeit vague, gives me a new sense of purpose. The open plaza with its strange grey and red scaffolding-like constructions, under which the buses park and depart, could be a larger-than-life demonstration of how to use the leftover plastic sprues of a scale-model kit. Even so, this sparse, functional ugliness possesses a comforting, Euro-futurist gloss. Also, getting the bus in a foreign land is always exciting.

Spirits lifted, I catch a bus headed for Noordwijk and wave the smallest gulden note I have at the driver, who looks at me with a certain pity as I try to say 'Noordwijk' as intelligibly as I can. A small square of thick paper is stamped and tossed into the till along with my change. I squeeze into a place near the centre of the bus. Now I can relax. My plan is to go to the end of the line to what I expect to be the seafront, as then the bus and I can't go any further, which is of course a perfectly good reason to get off any bus. Another cause for staying put soon becomes apparent: I have no idea what the driver is saying when he announces a stop. The shock of hearing Dutch spoken freely in its native setting and without recourse to any adaptations for an English listener brings on the awful realization that the names I see printed above the bus windows, presumably bus stops, bear no relation to the sounds the driver is making. Sod it. I'm staying on until I can't, until the end, which gives me time to think and plan my next steps. And seafronts the world over have pubs in which to do that, too.

The bus makes its final stop in a circular sunken concrete plaza next to the sea road. Families fresh from the beach pass by, carefree and smiling. Youths glide by on roller skates. There are people on bikes everywhere. The Dutch really like outdoor life, it seems. Humping my two huge bags, I sweat and stumble my way onto the promenade. At first impression, the row of pubs and cafes imparts a very utilitarian scene, a holiday-camp aesthetic. Built in the 1950s or 1960s, these establishments seem to have flats above them and boast terraces that look like conservatories without the roof. Pebble-dashed walls, concrete paving slabs and hardy pot plants on tables complete the look.

I go into the first bar that looks decent. Adjusting to the relative darkness of the interior, I notice a preponderance of polished wood and brass trimmings. Jolly music, a profusion of flowers in vases and fag smoke play strong supporting parts. I am served by a woman who is brisk, tall and blonde, and able to project friendliness as a way solely to get business done. The drinking feels 'public' and rehearsed, in contrast to the sullen marathons that constitute the drinker's day in northern English pubs. There is an unwanted undercurrent of jolliness, maybe tinged with melancholy: a distinct feeling that at some point the bar will break into a planned medley of songs from *The Sound of Music*. People look over at me as if I have escaped from a travelling fair. I sweat and fidget through a few pints, and get told, for no reason I can discern, to 'take it easy'.

After a few drinks I decide to get a taxi to the campsite. The taxi turns out to be a plush Mercedes, which is a mild shock. The driver doesn't bother with any small talk. We wind our way along sandy lanes lined with trees, the setting sun illuminating the large green fields. Paying the taxi fare is a bigger shock: it's not cheap here. Off goes the Merc, and I am alone in a wooded lane next to a large campsite bordered by huge box hedges. Now to business.

Entering a bungalow-ranch-style reception dwarfed by a monstrously large Dutch tricolour flapping overhead, I negotiate my keep with an unsmiling woman who obviously doesn't care about anything but my deposit. Eventually, after some tense back-and-forth and lots of pointing at bank slips and photocopied documents, I am able to prove who I am and the fact that I have paid for my digs upfront.

With a small key and local map in hand, I walk through the campsite in the gloaming and find my new home, a small, old, but serviceable caravan, and open the door. An air of brown, fusty gloom greets me. Turning on my torch doesn't help matters much. The fridge works but doesn't look well maintained. I bang my knees against the fittings that support a well-used French bed. My life is now just this, only this.

Darkness falls. The smells of kerosine and charcoal, cannabis, the nearby woods and the evening dew settling on the sandy ground encircle my caravan. I hear cries and screams and threats in a number of languages, ululations that only seem to increase in intensity over time. I curl up in the foetal position on the bed and wonder what the bloody hell I have done. And then I realize I don't have a pillow.

*

Sunday, 2 April 2000. It seems the Netherlands has become an uninhabited, post-apocalyptic country overnight. Tramping along the empty roads through a mist-laden landscape of greenhouses, fields and squat, shuttered houses, I see no one for at least two hours. The only things to stir my senses are the birds and the heady, slightly soapy smell of the massed rows of hyacinths coming into bloom in the fields around me. Are Sundays always like this here?

The reason for the mid-morning walk is to locate my new workplace, alongside scouting out bus routes and convenient places to shop, and similar practical chores. The address indicates it's in Lisse, a town about five miles away as the crow flies. Using the low-grade tourist map I picked up at the campsite, I inadvertently take the long route. After a two-hour walk I am mildly delirious. My stout leather brogues with commando soles, which seemed like such a good idea back in England, are turning my feet into steaming slabs of jellied flesh. Near the first place I can identify on my crap map, the Keukenhof, a tourist destination for tulip lovers the world over, I see my first humans. Tall, portly and ponderous, dressed alike in bright blues and greens, a small press of middle-aged couples lumbers towards me like swans climbing onto a riverbank. They take a moment to frown wonderingly and uncomprehendingly at me, a human clearly not of their kin, and one who seems to be blocking their way. Eyes flutter and are averted. Noses twitch, mouths purse. Their way of simultaneously blanking and judging me in complete silence is unnerving. They waddle by in a line, muttering. As if in warning of further trials to come, the sound of brass-band music wafts over from a neighbouring field. I need to keep moving.

It is approaching midday and my feet are negotiating with my stomach for some form of armistice. I walk into the sleeping town of Lisse and discover nothing of use to either. The edges of my sight are bordered by strong blues and yellows, my feet boil, everything feels slightly vertiginous. Stumbling into a side street, I am confronted by a brightly coloured and near-human-sized plastic statue of a conical bag of chips, with face and hands and bovver-booted feet. One of Chip Man's hands holds another, smaller bag of chips. What passes for Chip Man's hair is, I presume, given its colour, a representation of a large blob of mayonnaise. Despite my new-boy state in this land, I register that this is the place where the chips are.

Going inside, I wait to be served. Eventually a very grumpy looking blonde girl comes and stares at me. I ask for chips and elicit no recognizable response outside of a stare laden with a bank vault's worth of scorn. Pointing at Chip Man outside, I say 'chips?' in an enquiring voice. The girl turns away and prepares chips: none of the expected 'friendly Dutch' tropes here. What feels like an age passes before I am presented with a compact white tray stacked with French fries, atop of which wobbles a miniature Jeff Koons sculpture made entirely of mayonnaise. I spend the next ten minutes conducting an agonizing finger ballet in which I retrieve a fry from under the eggy oomska and then chew the sodden amalgam of reconstituted potato flour and fat to a dissatisfying conclusion. Or break my teeth on the salted rusty nails that also go by the names of 'chips' here. Either way, it's food.

After more walking I find the place I am working at the following day: a battleship-grey steel and concrete complex on a pretty, tree-lined backroad, opposite fields of narcissi and hyacinths just coming into bloom. An industrial estate set in a Dutch deer park. There are no bus stops nearby.

With an awful sense of dread, I realize there is little else to do now but walk back to the campsite along the same five or six miles I've already plodded.

An hour or so passes. Trudging through lanes surrounded by sandy fields alternately full of flowers on the point of blooming and hosting rows of greenhouses cruelly flashing the day's light back into my eyes, I am beginning to realize that walking to work will not be an option tomorrow. My feet are now officially bigger than my shoes and intent on telling me so with every step. Another mournful waft of brass-band music coming from a different direction from the first invokes a *Wicker Man*-esque panic in me. Are these sounds accompanying the ritual sacrifice of innocents? Or is this the only music approved here?

In my increasing delirium I register a gingerbread house along the side of the road. It is a riot of kitsch, its gateposts mounted by two painted and very camp statuettes of boys, both barefoot and posed in provocative attitudes. Each sports a tam-o'-shanter at a rakish angle. They look like figures who have just stepped out of a Gainsborough canvas. On the roof are various windmills and weathercocks on sticks and, emanating from some subterranean foundry of evil within the grounds, the sound of piped music of the sentimental, show-tune variety. The sky darkens. I speed up, feet or no feet.

Once back at the campsite reception I ask about hiring a bike. No hire, only sales. OK. Let's check out the bikes for sale. Most look like they were once the property of a churchwarden. Not having ridden a bike since 1979, I plump for the smallest, safest-looking, least fall-offable one on offer: an Airfix-scale model of a mountain bike for a large child, painted black. I won't die riding it, at least.

Another pressing issue is the state of my feet, which now feel like a pair of sea lions flopping about on a rock. Fumbling around in my caravan, I turn on my torch and use the spotlight to untie my laces and slowly prise my feet out of my steaming brogues. The torchlight gives the murky interior the kind of luminescence associated with a Rembrandt painting, some biblical elder discovering the word of Jehovah in a bush or on a rock. I, in a less exalted state, discover bubo-like swellings on my soles. In a flash of intuition, I rummage through my half-unpacked rucksack and find a tub of tea tree oil, a leaving present from a friend. Not really knowing what tea tree oil does but not wanting to upset the friend, I brought it with me, expecting to jettison it at some point. I massage the whole tub into my feet, and the unguent seems to work. Feeling a relief akin to a religious revelation, I happily throw the empty tub away and doze off on the cramped French bed, soundtracked by the gibbering howls of my unseen neighbours.

The next morning, forgetting that most bikes, even a child's bike, can move at three times walking speed, I arrive at my workplace ninety minutes early and wait for a sullen caretaker to open the main gates.

I am ready for work in a new country.

FACTORY POP

KASPER THE FOREMAN is a sturdy, moustachioed fellow with a flushed countenance. He walks with a disjointed gait, his arms dangling limply by his sides, as if his movements are driven by a battery in his back. Maybe years of lifting heavy things from concrete floors have made him walk like this. But he seems friendly enough as he takes me to my 'workstation', a large desk with a rubber floor mat next to a roller conveyor. On it are an air-pressure gun and a box of metal staples, a glue roller, with a small lake of glue in the container, a pile of compact and circular dried soil cakes, bags of luminous-yellow fertilizer tablets that look like a forgotten type of liquorice allsort, a roll of stickers with the word 'fragile' printed on them and a lot of photocopied instruction leaflets.

Kasper gives me a large wad of perforated address labels, which signify a specific order, and smiles. Here comes his prepared work speech. He tries to make it sound like friendly banter between men of the world, but there is always the understanding that he's the boss.

'It goes like this. You separate these labels, save this bit, and put the address on the glue roller and then on the top side of this box. Like this. You then put the boxes on a pallet. Like this.'

I start doing it 'like this', as Kasper says, and spend a rather enjoyable morning standing on the mat putting labels on boxes. The cardboard boxes are of various shapes and sizes and can be found stacked in unused bundles under some high scaffolding in a corner, near the onsite toilets. Each bundle is held together by a thin plastic strap that is easily twisted off but treacherously easy to trip over if left lying on the ground. The boxes are dry and smooth, and, in the cold of a spring morning, difficult to get a grip on, although it is easy to cut yourself on their sharp edges.

During this first shift I start to take in my surroundings: a high-roofed, grey factory space made of concrete and corrugated steel. Around me are a lot of plants, boxes and paper in various states of preparation. My new colleagues stand at workstations like mine or walk around the factory with plants and packaging in tow. Some look cool and interesting, others supremely fucked up, others still like the normal, nondescript factory hands I'd got to know while working in similar jobs in England. The noise is constant, comprising shouts and calls, the whir of the conveyor belt as a box slides down it, the buzz of the radio and the loud clacks and slaps of the pressure guns as the compressed air shoots a metal staple into a box side.

Now and again I get smiled at by someone passing by, or stared at by another. Some of the fucked-up ones look over in my direction but I'm not totally certain that what they are looking at is me. I soon clock that some of the calls hurled between workspaces are friendly prompts, looking to draw me into a conversation. One girl stands behind me. She seems a bright and cheerful soul who sometimes stops and looks into space, frozen in thought. After the usual pleasantries she tells me she's on the run from her husband, who wanted her to join a controlling Christian sect in Middlesbrough. Am I on the run too? No, just working here …

One other thing to note about my potential new pals: it seems that nearly everybody but me has a tattoo. Many prominently display a Celtic band on their upper arm, or some other signage, however small, on their necks or hands. One of those with a Celtic band is a Welsh lad with a rat-tail haircut. He is pushing boxed orders down one of the conveyor belts next to our workstations. At the end of the belt he stacks the boxes on pallets. Pausing by my table, he invites me to a drum circle in Leiden, only to warn me he doesn't drum but it's a good place to buy cheap booze and hot food. He then attempts to talk to me about Welsh history. Catching wind of our chat, Kasper looks over and frowns. My new friend then accidentally drops a box and uses the time in picking it up to finish what he's saying. The trick, it seems, is not to stop working but massage a conversation into the work. Good tip.

At ten o'clock Kasper shouts *pauze!* and we troop off to the canteen. Time for a sit-down: a welcome respite from standing on a rubber mat for hours. In the canteen I meet a new Dutch friend: a slim plastic cup filled, if you press the right button on the machine, with scalding hot coffee, tangy to the taste. Adding an air of sophistication to proceedings are milk powder, available in finger-length paper wraps, and sugar cubes, also wrapped neatly in paper. These two elements are brought into holy union by a third: a white plastic stirrer that many of my workmates play around with abstractedly, either in their cups or as something to hold between their teeth. Slowly people start to unwind. There is a noticeable difference between how this is done by us foreign workers, who are mostly loud and chatty, and the Dutch, who rarely communicate outside of grunts and nods. This small group of regulars and seasoned temporary workers sit happily enough on a couple of tables with their Tupperware boxes of sandwiches neatly placed in front of them. They let the supervisor, a loquacious lad from Kosovo, do all the talking.

A red-haired girl holds court around the long *buitenlander* table I'm sitting at. She had thrown friendly looks my way in the first shift and is obviously trying to sound me out, talking of raves back in 1988 in the Birmingham area. One of her stories involves being paralytically drunk while dressed as a chicken, which, she admits, isn't very ravey or New Age. Talk from others involves sardonic appraisals of the current sociopolitical state of Barcelona and the Irish border, or where to park a travelling van without getting hassle from the police or the locals. Fag smoke curls up to the low, stained ceiling tiles and the ashtrays fill. Standard cigarettes, however, are hardly seen. Rolling up, the act of *sjekkie draaien*, is the preferred form of smoking and a sort of unspoken communal practice that binds and reassures all workers: the Dutch in their 'simple but sensible folk of the world' guise, and the Irish, Catalans and Brits in their collective role as international savants. After coffee we are back on the floor, packing orders for flowers and bulbs going mostly to the United Kingdom.

By lunchtime I'm getting a handle on things, even if it is a very busy day. I learn by increments how to effectively wield the pressure gun at speed and how best to construct the differently sized and shaped boxes. Lessons include how to put a specific plant or bag of bulbs with the corresponding plastic pots and saucers and all the necessary papers in their box, then shut that box in a way that the order sits snug and immovable in its temporary cardboard home. The plants we pack are numerous and stored outside in a hedged-off section by the road or a huge refrigerator with a sliding door known as the cool cell. Here viola and petunia; young orange and lemon trees; blackberry, raspberry and yellow and red apple spurs; climbing roses (one of which is called Golden Showers); small trees such as eucalyptus, camellia and acer; and hundreds of miniature conifers of the leylandii variety all fight for space with each other in stacked trays and crates. In other crates lie bags of bulbs and roots, hostas, hens and chicks, irises and many other plant types, there to help create a cottage garden or bee sanctuary. These areas are overseen by a number of shifty-looking blokes with tinted glasses who mutter to the plants. They act as priests of a secret botanical sect: ones who are quick to anger, given the shouts and barked orders they give out to their Dutch colleagues. They have a couple of tough-looking, big-booted women helping them who bring the plants over to us and then stomp off without a word.

After lunch Kasper shows me how to put more exotic elements into the boxes, such as a plastic tortoise plant holder, another large flat box containing a sturdy metal frame that supports various breeds of climbing roses, and a primitive-looking and very breakable wooden wheelbarrow, an object that has a sour, pungent smell doubtless picked up from the shipping carton it arrived in. The business is also making some American test orders for a new mail-order client, a venture which has to be done 'properly'. In a display of trust (or maybe sadism) I am detailed to pack the test orders. One thing is immediately apparent: the customer names are discernibly different to those on the English address labels. So much so that I think I am hallucinating. After the calm of putting one hundred tortoises with a pot-shaped hole in their shell into a box with some seedlings, I find myself having difficulty understanding names and addresses in what is officially my own language. I throw the specially washed packs of bulbs into small boxes and send orders down the conveyor belt to a vast country full of Randys, Germaines, Diesels, Izanders, Tyces and Zebulons.

Apparently I'm quick on the uptake and Kasper, warming to me, comes over to my table and, blowing out his cheeks, which seem to sit on top of his moustache, starts to tell me of his hobbies. This is approved chatting time, as he's stopped working and expects me to stop too, to listen to him. I nod, not wanting to break his flow. His voice takes on a new tone: lyrical, mellifluous, crafty. 'You know, it goes like this. I like to fish. I'm pretty good. I know where the best carp are in the whole area, I have known them for years. They think they can get away from me. But I have a special plan. I am making a new fish food and they won't resist. Then I don't need to work here because I will make serious money.' Kasper looks at me radiantly. It seems wise to congratulate his coming triumph.

Other colleagues are less forthcoming on this first day. One is a Serge Gainsbourgian figure clad entirely in black, with fully laced-up para boots and a Lebanese shawl adding the sartorial highlights. He glides by, sitting on the front of an electric pickup truck known as a *pompwagen*. While doing so he adopts a nonchalant pose, as if steering a small motorboat on the Côte d'Azur. He eyes me up. His whole demeanour, the very cock of his head, his glinting earring, is doubtless assembled to advertise that he is 'obviously' French. Near the end of the day he starts to shriek out a series of loud, intermittent, unintelligible squawks, cackles and groans to no one in particular, and to the express annoyance of both Kasper and our Kosovan supervisor. Others seem interesting, if of another world entirely. One lad, the spitting image of John Lennon in his Winston O'Boogie phase, chucks me a gap-toothed smile and whizzes by, balanced on a *karretje*, a sort of small metal pickup trolley worked by a leaver. He spends a lot of time doing this. A tough, red-faced woman, the matriarch of a bunch of Catalans who are working together in a distant part of the factory, goes to the jakes frowning and comes back happily singing, waving a strip of what I take to be prescription drugs. I get a wink and an 'extra strong!', but no more.

Just before clocking-off time the Welsh lad comes over to my workstation and, while looking around for Kasper, starts telling me about what to expect over the coming season. He owns a travelling motorbike, meaning he gets around and knows this country, which, he tells me, is nothing like South Wales. Emboldened by Kasper's absence, he sits on the conveyor belt, running his hands up and down the rollers, and starts to fill me in on everything I should know about getting on in the Netherlands. This is very decent of him, but I suspect he just likes having a natter with a new face. I am warned we'll be working hard but won't be bored. At some point we will wrap mountains of fresh flowers for Mother's Day, loading the boxes onto lorries with their engines running. And we'll have a lot of overtime, sometimes sprung on us without notice at the end of a day. But overtime means a hot meal: something called *shoarma* and chips, with lots of mayonnaise on the side. According to this Welsh biker it is a gourmet feast and the only hot grub most people get, and why overtime is never really unpopular. Other good things about the work revolve around the many types of plants we'll pack over the coming months. I'm assured that these signs of a change in the seasons will be very tangible, even to the most spaced out of us (and apparently there are quite a number of spaced-out types working here). We both agree that plants and bulbs are there to give pleasure and sustenance: to heal, not to harm. No one wants to smash up a plant.

Another thing going for the spring season is the large number of official holidays in late April and May, meaning an extra day or so on the lash, hopefully extending a weekend. These causes for further bacchanalia, I am told, are known as *Pinksteren* (Whitsun) *Hemelvaartsdag* (Ascension Day), *Bevrijdingsdag* (Liberation Day), *Eerste en tweede paasdagen* (Easter) and, what sounds like the cherry on the cake, something called *Koninginnedag* (Queen's Day).

According to my new pal The Welsh Biker, these holidays are gloriously messy windows of opportunity. I can go to the non-locals pubs, of which there are many, and stay in them all day. And, if I get up early enough, I can get a bus to Haarlem or Leiden and visit an international pub in Amsterdam. Regardless, The Welsh Biker confirms these are days to get clean and be free of the itchy, slightly tangy dust, soil and glue residues that already feel like a new second skin. There is also the chance to do something more clandestine in the dunes or squats that pepper this area, if I'm into that, where it seems many like to spend their weekends in comatose chemical states. Not him, he's at pains to add: just beer and the odd psychedelic. He likes to look after himself.

The Welsh Biker's spiel means I can plug into wider unspoken hopes of the spring planting season: we are, after all, selling dreams of botanic fecundity to desiccated middle England and America through inserts in a mail-order magazine. Here, I gather, Arcadia is packed by a collection of tearaways, addicts, wannabe poets and escapees from all sorts of trouble: a polyglot tribe sending orders to Midwestern American housewives who want some glass-slipper, cow-on-the-canal version of a country that sleepwalks towards the never-never.

SUPERMARKET SWEEP

IT'S FRIDAY, five o'clock in the afternoon, 7 April 2000, and the end of my first working week in the Netherlands. Kasper yells thuis! and I put an aloe vera plant, plastic pot, dried soil block and some fertilizer into a box, close it with my airgun and gum the address label down. I pick up my stuff, clock out and walk off site, surrounded by my workmates, who mention things like 'the Sandpit' and '80 per cent pure' in their small talk. I'm not joining them so won't find out what these things mean just yet. No, I am getting the bus from Lisse to Leiden and then another to a place called Hazerswoude-Dorp to have supper and stay over with a gentle old couple of my acquaintance, both in their early seventies, called Jan and Esther. Jan and I were once colleagues when I was an international sales rep flogging hanging baskets to the retail gardening sector in the 1990s. Typically, he and Esther are doing the decent thing and checking that I'm settling in. The child's bike I bought to cycle to work, which I hope one day to raise the saddle on, will be tethered to a tree overnight near Lisse's bus station. Getting to the station means taking the backroads to the town centre. The Scouse Philosopher is going my way. I decide to push my bike while walking into town with him.

The Scouse Philosopher is an affable six-footer from Liverpool who seems to favour dressing like Ali G. His act, if it is one, includes a loud and repeated championing of the charms of Britney Spears's glorious pop music. It's disarming enough. He's certainly a clever lad and not shy of telling me about his current 'business problem', which is how best to secretly transport a lucrative stash of recreational drugs back to England. His favoured method is to swallow the drugs in a condom, aiding its passage through his alimentary canal with copious amounts of yoghurt. He asks me: should he first practise with grapes? The resulting discussion on the relative laxative properties of dairy, preparing the stomach with the fruit of the vine and what measures would negate the premature passing of the condom is carried out in some detail as we walk into Lisse. I certainly don't envy his situation. The Scouse Philosopher tells me of the excitement of a previous run when he heroically made the first public convenience without the sheath bursting in his stomach. He also explains in some detail the methods to stop his cargo disappearing into the Mersey. Clearly, factory life is a portal to many careers.

The bus pulls into Hazerswoude-Dorp. It's a small, nondescript, outsized village with lots of post-war housing surrounded by a wide expanse of fields and canals. There is a strong feeling that nothing ever happens here, though I can sense that many of its inhabitants like it that way.

At Jan and Esther's I sit down to a traditional Dutch meal of tasty and unpretentious veg and potato mash with gravy and fried pork cuts. We have a couple of bottled beers in glasses, and follow them with a coffee and a small chocolate on a dainty china plate. The coffee comes with a tiny ornate metal spoon with a coat of arms on the tip of the handle. Esther has a small liqueur and rolls her eyes in mock horror as she pushes the boat out. We watch television, specifically a programme about the latest happenings in the world of Dutch showbiz, where perma-smiling people boasting teeth that could bite through a turnip talk incessantly about the latest entertainment news. As if to balance out the soft-focus razzmatazz, we also get segments featuring two wild-looking, forty-something blokes with sunglasses and moody demeanours. One may be called Herman and the other André. The one called André seems close to tears throughout and is squeezing a can of Heineken in his hand, fearful of letting it go. The other fellow, Herman, seems more of a nutter. Even though I hardly know a word of Dutch, it's clear he's reeling off some fragmented spiel about rock and roll. Esther sucks her teeth and frowns. Jan shakes his head angrily, bristling with indignation.

'Ach, these two, they are always drunk, even on television. It's disgraceful.'

I stay the night, sleeping on the couch, and pass a pleasant Saturday morning visiting Jan's son, who runs a plant-export company in a nearby village. He's busy but finds time to share a carton of buttermilk with us and his own family. We stare out in silence over his yard, watching the antics of his pet goats. It's been a pleasant break and an insight into how the Dutch quietly get on with their lives. And I am beginning to understand more fully what people in this country mean by taking it easy: namely, sitting down and not talking too much. There is no rush, it seems, outside of getting to the shops before they close. Which reminds me: I have to go shopping for the week ahead. The previous week has seen me eat in small cafes, snackbars and bakeries in Lisse before cycling back to the caravan, but I can't afford cafe-priced meals for much longer. It's time to brave a Dutch supermarket, a new experience. Come on, man, you can do it.

With an hour or so to spare before my bus, I enter a small, low-roofed supermarket on the edge of Hazerswoude-Dorp, conveniently near the stop for Leiden. Walking through the doors leads me into a wholly new world, and one that I hadn't entirely bargained on. Space feels distorted: the shelves are far too high and close together, and the narrow aisles give a feeling of being trapped in a maze. The Dutch signs are of little use. Even being close to the product doesn't help as many articles are stacked and cramped into irretrievable spaces, and, when I work out what some of the wares are, there seems to be no logic in their placement. The experience is simultaneously like the descriptions of shops in Dickens novels and, given the glare of the strip lighting, a customs interrogation room on a border. I stare at everything a little harder but, away from the usual incitements to buy, the packaging gives little away. After a while I decide to go round the aisles once more, intent on seeing where things are and with a resolve to grab what I need, come what may. There are many powders and spices and a profusion of baking and dairy products, some of which seem to need a special introductory course to eat. Others have names that appear simple or even childish, which makes me wonder why anyone would put such things in their mouths. I don't want any of those.

I start to sweat as I realize I must look like the world's worst shopper, or worse a loiterer, and in here of all places, a sedate village supermarket with a number of respectable middle-aged and elderly people buying groceries. It's doubtful these people care about me in any case as they're probably exercising their right to 'take it easy'. This thought just compounds the awful sense of being very alone in a world surrounded by food. To make matters even more unpalatable, the place is drowning in soft, sickly commercial pop music. There is no escape from the awful drone, given the speakers pumping it out are snugly fitted into the roof. In between lashings of schmaltz, the radio station knocks out a regular jingle that tells the shoppers, including two ladies wrapped up to withstand a winter storm and buying milk by the pallet-load, that it is 'sharing all the good times'. I've been in here less than half an hour and have heard that entreaty three times.

Suddenly a strange sensation of being underwater, on the edge of a waking dream, or being mildly sedated while in a dentist's chair, starts to unnerve me. Time to get a grip. I resolve to buy some things and start with the most immediately recognizable foodstuffs. My main choices lie between a dizzying array of raw, root or canned vegetables or a wall of dairy. I play safe and buy cheese, milk, bread and cured meat. Everything else feels too off-beam. Sweating with indecision at the meat counter, I buy what I believe to be six ounces of cured squirrel.

On the buses to Leiden and then Lisse, I clasp my shopping like gold dust wrung from a mountain stream. Back on my bike in Lisse, I also discover that cycling into the wind with a shopping bag on each handlebar and an overnight bag on my back is an experience to be avoided. No matter: I press on. There are only three miles to go. Halfway home I find myself passing a house I have noticed before. It's on a bend in the road that also marks a cross-section of small irrigation canals that flow between the fields. Despite being the end dwelling in a small row of houses that overlook open fields on every side, this house emanates an aura of fusty gloom unique to it alone. This is because an unusual car is often parked outside: some small, squat model of indeterminate make from the 1960s. It looks like the sort of car a spy or terrorist would drive: certainly one owned by a malcontent. Off-white due to layers of congealed grime, it has also not been washed for a long time, maybe for a reason. There may even be green mould on the bumper and parts of the underside. And, on this barren, blustery Saturday afternoon, there is a man in the car, sitting in the driver's seat, not moving and staring straight at me as I draw level. He's wearing a trilby and has a heavy, dark moustache. I prepare myself for something to happen but nothing does: the man continues to sit immobile and look ahead. At the moment I pass I notice something else, crawling out of one of the canals and onto the bank. Something strange, foreign: a memory of other, more ancient worlds. That thing is a large terrapin, glistening from its recent dip. It looks around and, finding nothing of note, slides back into the water. Despite the wind and the luggage I'm carrying, I pedal that little bit harder. Only a mile or so to go.

CHIP MAN MEETS MUTE SWAN

CARAVAN CAPERS

THREE O'CLOCK, Tuesday morning, 18 April 2000. I am brought to my senses by a battering at my caravan door and light against my window.

'Wake up! Police!'

It really is that thing of fable: a police raid. On a Monday night of all nights. A torch is flashed in my eyes and a police dog snarls and snaps in unnervingly close proximity to my crown jewels as I stumble back and search for my passport, which I then present.

'Thank you, sir.'

I am handed back my passport. The door is shut. The dog's righteous ire is saved for some Polish lads a few doors down who haven't got the necessary three-month work permits. The campsite owner is there behind the cops, shaking his head and looking as if he's been conned by these lads, after all he's done for them.

*

When I get back from work in the evening the campsite owner is strolling around, talking to people, maybe reassuring himself he's done enough to cover his own tracks in the eyes of his tenants. Rubbing his chin thoughtfully and putting on a show of magnanimity to the quieter set of campers and Dutch families who rent the adjacent chalets, he explains how this kind of thing normally never happens, but he's a man of the world and there are always crazy people to contend with when you're in his line of business. Plus those boys hadn't paid their rent. Later I see him laughing and joking with the new Polish cleaner girls.

So far the campsite hasn't been a hotbed of action. It's a place where, for a relatively cheap fee, I can attend to my Five Basic Needs. These are: a sheltered sleep, a relatively safe environment to store my kit and grub, having washing facilities to hand, rest and recreation in the closest village (Noordwijkerhout) or the surrounding nature, and an official enough address for work purposes. A home it is not.

I'm beginning to realize that campsites are weird places when they're not employed for wholesome holiday fun. For those of us living here while working or looking for work, there is a distinct feel of the wider site being an open prison that has been partially taken over by the inmates. I've been giving this some thought these first few weeks and have come to the conclusion that I have landed in an out-of-the-way sociopolitical petri dish from the previous decade.

Firstly, given the amount of raver types who amble about, many wearing loon pants and tees far too big for them, a few even sporting kaftans, there is a strong afterglow of post-1988 acid-house idealism abroad; then, given the sizable Polish and smaller Czech and Balkan contingents, a certain post-Soviet, post-war economic necessity. Closer to home, the number of Ulster accents and single girls, and a couple of out-and-out wannabe Begbie-from-*Trainspotting* types, hints at both a quiet desperation driven by the fallout from domestic and political troubles and low-grade forays into illegality. I'm not sure who the midnight howlers and screamers are: I'll take a guess and say those on a bad trip, or who have tried to rob from the Polish and are being dealt with by that tribe's unofficial security. This is the heady sociocultural cocktail, with me as its random demographic outlier, that finds itself nestling in the shadow of the glorious deciduous woods and sand dunes just off the Dutch coast. The camping area given over to us plebeians contains a host of squat single caravans set out in rows in just over a hectare of grassland, with a water pump and a vending machine. We are cordoned off from the gentler holidaymakers by a box-hedge boundary that is too high to peep over with a root system that seems to contain a trillion red ants, and above which the smoke of a thousand joints and some appalling attempts at cooking settles glumly in a desultory, self-satisfied haze.

Weary after a broken sleep and a day's toil I enter my caravan and slump onto the edge of my bed. I eat some bread and cheese and a hunk of *ontbijtkoek*, a sweet loaf-like dry cake which I now regard as a staple food. What to do tonight, the night after the morning of the raid? Well, like other nights, I can sit in my caravan. But sitting in a caravan for more than a few hours is a difficult thing to do, unless you are dog-tired, stoned immaculate or have a pressing need to lie low. For one thing, given their metal frame, caravans are never the right temperature. And when you are six foot four inches tall, as I am, sitting in one for any stretch of time can lead to a certain stir-craziness: the feeling you are living in a tin-can panopticon. A line from the New Order song 'Every Little Counts' has started to haunt me over this last week or so: 'I think you are a pig, you should be in a zoo.' That's caravan life, all right. You can stare at the plastic, wood-look coating of the walls, the battered fridge and cramped fittings and allow yourself to sail away on a sea of meaningless half-thoughts and frustrations. You can listen to the BBC World Service, which over time reveals itself to be a mere amplifier for a series of sociocultural set pieces. Or you can smile wanly at your own self-righteousness and nestle down on the coarse brown and orange fustian of the French bed with an improving book. It's the sort of self-help strategy driven by no noble reason outside of avoiding more boredom. In fact, the overwhelming dullness invoked by being good, by trying to improve yourself, by taking the chance to 'get it together' in an ageing caravan in an uncaring foreign land, surrounded by relative strangers, some of whom are negotiating their own levels of craziness and marginalization with mixed results, has nothing to recommend it.

The prospect of idleness presents itself. To stave that off, I try to continue learning Dutch from a book while glancing out over a row of grimy caravans, flicking ants off the page. I make the noises suggested, all of which seem to stretch my throat and use muscles in my tongue that I never knew existed. I learn a set of rudimentary sentences that will establish friendly relations with the Dutch and ensure I can feed and water myself. Taken collectively, they sound like a procession of coughs, caws, honks and sneezes. I give up after an hour, my larynx now raw with exertion.

Feeling rather foolish, and hoping that no one has heard me, I stare out of the window. I think of my grandparents and their parents and the privations they went through: Gallipoli and Kaiserschlacht, the Blitz, coal mines and various heavy industries, cold-water taps, outside netties, TB, Spanish flu, debilitating cancers, shell shock, premature Alzheimer's, grinding poverty and soul-destroying factory work.

Someone, somewhere, probably one of those who wears a kaftan, is playing Bob Marley. I have paid for three full months of this, with an option to extend for another three. Then I will have to find somewhere more permanent. No wonder people in this game get completely out of it, keep moving on or look for a local to settle down with. A temporary stay until the next temporary stay. A hamster-wheel economy. Survival becomes a matter of staving off subconscious dreads like these, and realizing that boredom here becomes an entity in itself, a squat imp that waits patiently in the corner until you call.

A more immediate antidote to my rising angst is to check up on my fellow campers. I am slowly making one or two friendships here. I wander over to see some pals from the factory, a pair of Irish girls who are renting a double caravan. One's taking a break from her man and kid back on the northern side of the border. The other is from the south-west of the country and full of ideals and plans about smashing theocracy and the patriarchy. There is a mini sound system playing the *doof doof* music that is the staple of those independent local radio stations that consider themselves more 'with it'. Nothing is really worth talking about, outside of swapping a desultory few words about work opportunities in various factories. It's a midweek night in any case, and both seem content just getting stoned to the never-ending pulse of the future.

I pop in on a Scottish lad who is quietly preparing for the revolution by reading *American Psycho* and some tome registering the cruelties of Edward Longshanks. We talk of the diverse accents of Ulster, and which of these can be attributed to Scottish migrations. It's more of a one-sided lecture than a talk as it's a subject I know nothing about. The Scots lad's pal, a softly spoken Ulsterman who never takes his sunglasses off, is tripping mildly on the step of the caravan. His jaws rotate to the beat coming from his handheld radio. Looking on, it's hard to escape the feeling they have both taken a conscious step to live out their take on a Kerouac novel.

Maybe I should go for a walk. Taking the road towards the village of Noordwijkerhout and turning back to look over the complex, I contemplate the psychic properties of the campsite. I suddenly giggle and imagine myself as some low-grade Jonathan Meades character, explaining this particular aspect of *uber*-Dutchness on an artsy TV programme to a disbelieving outside world:

The entrance is welcoming enough in its faux-rustic way (a newish house planted snugly in the lee of a dune replete with Dutch flag, wooden gate and a neat garden). Adjacent to the raggedy settlement the foreign workers find themselves unceremoniously dumped in are greener, more well-appointed plots. Here stand the places for the car and caravan dreams of middle-aged holidayers. These groups enjoy the 'simple life' of dune walking and drinking coffee in a well-appointed beach hut. The men of this tribe often boast inordinately long legs and are proud to show them, favouring ancient, battered shorts to go with pumps and well-laundered T-shirts.

A stone's throw separates these Jolly Spartans from rows of plasticized wood-and-concrete chalets with a place for the family car and a small area in front that normally accommodates a barbecue set. Even though it is early in the season, a few enthusiastic pioneers have started firing these up, preparing funeral pyres of pig and cow flesh, greased by the twin lubricants of mayonnaise and salad oil.

A field further along reveals camping nirvana: a number of rows of mini-houses, smug and gleaming, obviously fitted with all mod cons. However modern, these abodes uniformly ape, even if only in spirit, the nativist idyll of a seaman's charming clapboard cottage. These odes to the region's seafaring history nestle unobtrusively amongst sylvan glades and more native expressions of topiary. Even with history on her side, Silvanus isn't ever really allowed to run wild here, as these settlements had a feeling of being scrubbed and snipped each morning, before sunup.

One-nil to me and my imagination. I carry on walking along the cycle path towards the village, looking over the small roadside dykes at the compact little farms and stables. Everything feels settled, even if these brick houses, with their long wooden sheds and greenhouses, are modest enough in size and unremarkable in aspect. Their magic comes from the fact that these settlements have been here forever and are unattainable to outsiders: claiming the land they stand on for themselves and their loved ones alone. Places, for the owners at least, of warmth and safety. Oh, to have a real roof over my head.

The village heaves into view. After a five-minute stroll, while marvelling at the way Dutch gardens and front-window decorations have a way of shamelessly imitating each other in virtually every aspect without recourse to internecine violence, I decide not to hit a pub and turn back.

Framed by the setting sun, I see the campsite owner with his wife atop a gig, the horse moving at a steady canter. I'm ignored as they trot past me. This display of rustic contentment is also for the locals only. Anyway I'm currently of no importance to their worldview as I've paid them my rent this week.

It's now night, the moment when the panopticon qualities of the site come fully into play. Unwanted visits are common by night, involving drunken or tripping people who have missed the bus to Leiden or Haarlem looking for a place to squeeze into to keep warm and dry. Despite many doors being closed, there is always the feeling of being watched, sized up as prey. Then there is the low-level sonic pollution to ignore: the disembodied screams and yells or sudden, unexpected blasts of terrible New Age dance music, often turned up to combat a peculiar drug-induced deafness. I turn over and sleep on my rolled-up coat and remember it's Easter on Friday.

*

Easter Sunday, 23 April 2000, Common Era. Sunday is most definitely a day of rest in the Netherlands. On this national holiday the land seems even more deserted, resembling nothing less than the aftermath of an alien abduction on a national scale. Easter Sunday in England usually sees a roaring trade in chocolate and other processed goods at roadside garages. They can't be that religious here, surely. Waiting until eleven o'clock I decide to stroll into Noordwijkerhout and get a bus to either Haarlem or Leiden, whichever comes first.

A few hundred yards up the road is a cafe that sits on the intersection of a T-junction and a sharp bend in the road that follows the shape of the dunes. It's a white-painted joint with a glass-partitioned terrace that backs onto a larger hotel. Carved totemistic wooden sculptures adorn the terrace area, including one of a huge, stylized poodle which, given its pronounced brow, has the air of an Easter Island statue about it. The place is just opening, sing hosanna. I decide to treat myself to a coffee. I have barely taken a seat in anticipation of the usual long wait for service when, as if by magic, the terrace is filled with what feels like a plague of cyclists, clanking stiffly towards me on their specially designed racing shoes. All are middle-aged, if not senior men, wearing a lot of coloured Lycra and each still with his helmet on. The profusion of white and grey moustaches, wind-beaten faces and helmets makes the group look faintly military, and they would resemble a company of psychedelic soldiers from a Beatles film if they didn't give off the feeling of utmost propriety and self-satisfaction. This is evidently a sport approved by the Lord. They settle down on the terrace chairs almost in unison, like a flock of birds descending on a field, and begin a loud debate interspersed by a lot of staring at the menus on the tables. I may have very little idea what is being said but I have already encountered this local habit of unnecessary prevarication when faced with choosing from a menu.

Why does it take people so long to read or choose from menus in this land? Surely to goodness there's no trap lying in wait. Another phalanx of bikers pedals by. 'My' bikers stare out, unconcerned. I get my coffee and immediately order another. It's not often I get a hot drink outside of the processed coffee at work; and after all, the Son of God has risen on this day so I will just this once push the boat out. The waiter asks one of the cyclists what they want. As there is no consensus the waiter agrees to return. Which leads to more pointing and frowning at the cards. After another five minutes or so I realize the whole thing is making me nervous. It's not as if, like me, they have to guess wildly and hope the ordered drink is not inappropriate or transgressing some local custom, like the 3 per cent-strength Oud Bruin bottled beer I ordered last week in Haarlem: a beer which, according to the laughing barman who served me, is the traditional choice for pregnant women. These gentlemen grew up here. They're sitting on the terrace of a Dutch cafe which, at this time and on this day, would normally serve coffee and tea or a soft drink. What other purpose is there for being here? After another ten minutes or so, the waiter comes back and the group orders coffees and teas. Is this actually a display of sitting, of being seen to be sat, that I am witnessing? A throwback to some form of token overlordship where the peasants may toil in the fields but the gentlefolk can rest in the knowledge that God will take care of all? I don't bother to ask and stroll on towards the bus stop.

Later that evening, on the bus back from a day exploring Leiden, I bump into a young Irish couple who I got to know in one of the village pubs. They are a cool pair, slightly hippy in demeanour, and intelligent and funny to boot. The lad has been in town visiting friends in one of the Leiden squats. He tells me there's a party in the Sandpit: why not tag along? I've overheard talk about the Sandpit, a large clearing in the dunes not far from my caravan site that, unsurprisingly, resembles a giant sandpit. The dunes stretch for miles, from Den Haag right up the North Holland coast. A natural barrier to the sea, they are also an important nature reserve, full of many types of fauna and flora. All in all a glorious place to relax and a real antidote to the factory grind. The couple aren't going for the red squirrels and nightingales, though. Apparently there will be people there with a sound system and recreational drugs. I've got a few beers in my caravan so I will content myself with those and meet them there.

Walking through the wooded dunes at dusk is tricky without a torch. The trees, tall for this part of the Netherlands, cast dark shadows which fill the hollows of the rises. The ground is very uneven: hummocks fall away into steep dips without warning. Stumbling over roots while watching out for burrows and soft sand is another hazard. But it's a relaxed scene that greets me at the Sandpit. Things are benevolent enough, the *doof doof* never really getting too loud, and people are chatting and relaxing, with some joshing about. Plus, if things get too intense the Sandpit is big enough to keep out of the way of the main action. I see my workmates Winston O'Boogie and Serge Gainsbourg are here, also lurking in the shadows. We smile and nod. I've got to know Winston a bit this last week or so. A serious and sensitive soul from Ulster, he combines an interest in archaeology with heavy music such as Slayer and a penchant for caning it on exotic substances. He's a sympathetic listener, with a dry sense of humour and a sadness that follows him about. I really like him but feel he doesn't want too many mates. Gainsbourg is as Sphinx-like as ever. They're busy talking about something that is 'nearly pure'. I leave them to it and happily slump on the lee of a mound and sup one of my cans, looking on.

Time passes on this easy-going scene; it's so restful that I fall into a reverie. When fully awake again I think about the placid calm of the cyclists deliberating over their menus. Would they be so unconcerned when looking on at this scruffy press of people, happily rolling around on the ground and laughing silently at the night sky?

A girl with pink hair jumps out of a group of recumbent figures and runs across the clearing at pace, whooping and jabbering indecipherably. She is followed by a lad who skips clumsily behind her. Most others remain supine, but I notice the music has gone up a notch, the incessant beat beginning to tremor through the wide hollow. Some people are flashing torches around to the accompaniment of screeches and maniacal laughs and angry shouts. Now and again a figure is framed momentarily in the light, and the tableau freezes in my mind, the gesturing figures in the gloom resembling those in Goya's witch paintings. Still, the deaf Goya could at least content himself with depicting rural satanism having been spared the joys of happy hardcore.

As I can't really join in, most people being too far gone for any form of communication, to relax I leave and walk along a path. Finding a place to sit and take stock, I slowly succumb to the healing rhythms of Dame Nature until I feel a hot, panting breath and a low groan behind me, rolling round to be confronted by a giant bloodhound, its frowning owner not far behind. Doubtless he thinks I am a vagabond. I freak out. Time to head home.

*

Eight o'clock in the morning on Wednesday, 26 April. We shuffle to our posts, about to start work on what will be another day of catching up on the post-Easter orders. We already know there will be overtime tonight as there was last night, as the *Koninginnedag* holiday is this coming weekend and many people, including lorry drivers, will be taking Friday off as a warm-up. Some may even take the Monday off too. Not us, though: we are packing five days' work into three mad days plus a normal day of being very busy. Late but smiling, evidently lost in his own thoughts, Winston O'Boogie rolls up through the lorry bay. He wasn't about yesterday and is immediately confronted by our furious floor boss, full of righteous Balkan ire.

'Where were you yesterday? I need everyone here this week. One more day off and you're sacked.'

'Wait, it's Tuesday, isn't it?'

Arms out wide, a look of shock on his face, Winston O'Boogie is not trying to deceive anyone, that is clear.

Flummoxed, muttering threats to no one in particular, my boss leaves it, defeated.

HOLIDAY

HEMELVAART, PINKSTEREN, PAASDAGEN AND *KONINGINNEDAG*. These are the four horsemen of the drink-and-drugs apocalypse.

It's early Saturday morning, 29 April 2000. I am standing on the open square that acts as Noordwijkerhout's bus terminal with my pal An Garda Síochána, a jolly, red-faced son of County Cork who I like a lot. The reason for the meetup on this particular Saturday is that it's *Koninginnedag*, the Dutch Queen's official birthday. Along with a number of regular drinkers from the village pub I spend a lot of time in, De Schotse Bar, known to us as the Scots Bar, we are waiting for the bus to Haarlem train station en route to Amsterdam.

Koninginnedag is a red-letter day in the Dutch calendar. The good folk of Noordwijkerhout are already celebrating it by racing huge tractors around the bus plaza. This open square also boasts a sound system and a loudspeaker rigged up to a PA, through which some official is excitedly calling out the scores of the tractor battle. It looks a laugh but, outside of the PA guy and the drivers, there is no one about. We forgo the fun and get on the bus to Haarlem.

Haarlem's beautiful nineteenth-century station is packed full of tall, giddy youths wearing anything they can find that is orange, not discounting toilet seats and table cloths. Fake furs, face paint and boiler suits are very popular. This young crowd brays loudly and indiscriminately at anyone and anything in their path. Beer cans and fag butts are everywhere, and there is a distinctive olfactory fug hanging over the whole station area, comprising elements of *Cannabis sativa*, urine, lager gases and various highly aromatic fried foods. We get on an overcrowded train to the capital. The constant noise, the sound of pressure released by real excitement and expectation, is remarkable. It's like listening to an over-compressed, airless recording of waves rolling in on a beach.

Tumbling out of a packed and smoky train at Amsterdam Centraal, An Garda Síochána tells us to hold each other's hands so as not to get lost in the scrum. The wall of noise hits us as we leave the station. It seems that Amsterdam is literally shaking with the reverberations of the revellers, a city wobbling around its own orbit. There is a miasma floating over everything we see: a throbbing potage of fumes, fires, ambient noise and wild vibrations emanating from the ever-growing press of people. This is a party on a grand scale. Queen Beatrix having any hand in shaping its character is, to these eyes, doubtful. We head towards the nearby red-light district. Across the water of the Damrak, gangs of revellers lean out of rows of creaky-looking windows, waving and hollering at anything and anyone: a frantic display of bonhomie. The smell of marijuana, burning petrol and flare smoke is ever present, and the noise of a thousand sound systems atomizes the air we breathe.

We turn past the Grasshopper pub, a well-known English-speaking outpost that seems to act as a tollhouse for the depravities just beyond it. Gangs of sharp-eyed English, Scottish, Welsh and Irish men, all looking like they're in mufti for the day, stand on guard outside, best trainers on and legs planted in a wide, defensive stance. This crowd shares two sorts of haircut: Norman knight or ponytailed buccaneer. None of them are drug or sex tourists; they display none of the naive braggadocio of the English day-tripper lads, even if both groups share certain codes of behaviour. All these lads work here, in various trades. All are clearly revelling in the sense of anarchy and noise.

We turn onto the Warmoesstraat, a cramped and dark street that acts as one of the main arteries of the red-light district. Our first stop is a place called Hill Street Blues, a joint that has been kitted out as a classic dive bar. Over time it's clearly sunk into the role allotted to it. Covered in graffiti, with a profusion of ripped photos on the wall and knackered, fag-burned seating, Hill Street Blues is a handy place to have that first pint in, or light up if you so wish. The attraction for those coming in from the Bollenstreek area is that you are bound to bump into someone you know from a previous packing season or a holiday in Goa or Thailand.

The place has a glorious view over the water on the Damrak too, which currently looks as if it's hosting a sea battle, what with the plumes of smoke and small craft drifting over the surface. It is smoky but not unpleasantly so. Piercing strips of daylight illuminate the mist of beer fug, fag and joint smoke and the haze from the street. Framed by these vapours, as if aware that the soft light shows them off to good effect, the clientele do their best to look battered but interesting. Fallen angels in repose. Faces are lined, wary; some look like they've been varnished. Various Celtic and Maori-style tattoos are casually displayed. There is a distinct sense that no one has put their best, clean-pressed shirt on in here.

I listen to a bunch of lads talking loudly about where best to go later in the day. Lots of intense confirmatory nods and loud yelps push the 'this is the place you get most wrecked' narrative along, as people compete to show how cognizant they are of Amsterdam. I have lost An Garda Síochána and the rest of the Noordwijkerhout lot. They are probably in Durty Nelly's, a lively Irish bar near the Oude Kerk, or The

Greenhouse Effect, an easy-going coffee shop you can drink in. There is an outside chance they will have stumbled into one of the Bulldog pubs, places where pasty men in tracksuits glower over pints, looking like squat bags of cement left out to sag in the rain.

Never mind where they are. I go back to listening in to the conversation, now led by a skinny man with bleached hair, a jumper that looks like his dog sleeps on it and an oversized earring, who barks out a series of commands at the group, confirming his every utterance with a set of challenging smiles and nods. We are told where to buy the best drugs, where the stabbing took place last week, why the city isn't as good as it was in 1987, and so on.

One of the great consolations of Amsterdam is that, in this part of the city especially, you are surrounded by loudmouthed English speakers who all somehow claim the red light as some form of personal colony. It can be irritating but it's also prime-time entertainment if you allow this oddly competitive scene space and time to play itself out in front of you. The trick is not to answer back. I imagine that most of these 1990s street hounds, propping up the many bars with their baccy pouch and skins laid out in front of them, secretly want to act out their cameos in *Trainspotting* or *The Beach*.

I head back out into the street, now packed with even more people, and end up in front of a nondescript boozer with a perma-grinning Ulsterman and a silent, scowling lad in a Celtic shirt. The Ulsterman talks with pride about his freshly shaved head.

'Feel it! Smooth, eh? Lovely and SMOOTH.'

He's a nice enough lad, if somewhat the worse for wear. He's also got a tattoo of a snarling leopard on his arm. I don't ask about the provenance of the leopard, but find out he works at a big bulb-export business in Hillegom. The fact we both work in the bulbs gives us something to talk about, as I'm not sure 'back home' is a wise or relevant topic with these two. A succession of doleful-looking Indian lads come up, trying to sell us roses or offering to take our picture. We decline. Other men, hands in pockets and with their hoods up, walk up to us and whisper an assortment of what sound like commands.

'White. Ket. Charlie. Coke. E. Brown. China. Whizz.'

Our silence means they move on to the next group.

At this point, realizing I've spent something like five hours on the same street, I move on in the company of two lads from Middlesbrough who have also been offered the chance to feel the Ulsterman's head. Both Clevelanders are squatting somewhere in Leiden. They seem handy and wised up, good enough to tag along with. It's past seven o'clock and there is a feeling in the air that the day's character is changing. The clumsy effervescence you associate with day revellers, the couples and younger crowds who normally don't drink, is beginning to disappear. Those boozers who are already boozed will get more so, and fall over in the street or get carted off.

Middlesbrough #1 notes that there is another party about to start, maybe more intense, driven by those intent on having a night out, on claiming their rightful share of fun. He points out new groups amongst the increasingly ragged and staggering groups of lads of what look like Turkish, Somalian, Surinamese and SSS and ABC islanders weaving in and out of the Brueghelian tableau. Middlesbrough #1 tells me that these gangs are the Schiphol baggage handlers, the road menders, the hospital cleaners, the tax-free crowd, the lads the *uitzendbureau* 'back to work' teams drop off and pick up in vans; the Polish gangs who live on the campsites for three months and break their backs and knees in the fields; an unseen army of workers that silently helps to maintain the Dutch state.

Walking towards the end of the Warmoesstraat and heading through an increasing press of people, the three of us pass through a narrow gap between two distinct crowds. On one side of the street, in front of a wide and tall black door with silver letters saying COCKRING, a gang of mostly Dutch lads saunter about, laughing, flexing and watching the passers-by, supremely confident in themselves. On the other side is a bunch of forty-something, paint-spattered arty types of all sexes and sizes, and some punks too. Neither group looks like they will kick off, but don't seem particularly welcoming either. We negotiate them like they're Scylla and Charybdis. For a few seconds we are checked out in minute detail by both groups as we pass through, then almost instantly ignored again.

We turn left and left again. Amsterdam now is like a fantasy, a series of destinations in a game of Dungeons and Dragons. In the gloaming, various portals present themselves. We sample what is on offer over the coming hours.

Some boozers look terrifying, boasting huge window fronts partially covered by a name in gold letters, yellowing lace curtains hanging on a brass rail, the windowsills full of gnarled potted plants and strange statuettes. We try the busiest of these. The noise is incredible in this brown-painted bar: a shifting sustained wail of half-sung plaintive laments, a mix of fag-cracked altos and burping tenors, their ululations running like Morse code from one end of the bar to the other. The singing is driven sometimes by a number on the jukebox, sometimes by a desperate cry from an unseen corner. No pints in here, just the small glasses, fluitjes or vaasjes, their contents disappearing all too quickly.

The underlying melancholy gets to us after a while and we leave. We cross a canal bridge, avoiding a man in a motorized wheelchair who seems to be concealing a pistol in his tracksuit top. Other places seem desperate in their attempts to have a good time. We enter one joint, a postmodern wood-and-plastic cave with a huge screen projecting a film of a green nymph with wings sitting on a toadstool.

There are a handful of people in here, desperately dancing to the drill-time inanities of happy hardcore. None are in any sense sober. I see an old couple pull knives on each other in slow motion. Getting a pint in for sanity's sake, I turn around and bump into a nice southern Englishman I know who lives on the outskirts of Noordwijkerhout. He appears to have risen in a mist from the floor, like a member of the undead. He is also tripping the light fantastic: his eyes bulge and his normally trim beard looks like it is charged with static electricity. A serene Dutch girl holds on to him, and I notice strands of her long hair have rolled joints tied into them. The place is a blazing vortex of citrus and candyfloss colours, amplified thuds and sickly, processed squeals. Mr South is screaming a message of love and peace at me while his eyes continue a tour of their sockets. His upper lip displays a calcified chalk line of cocaine residue that starts at his septum. We eventually make our excuses and leave.

Back on the street, other alleyways suggest themselves, each revealing staggering bodies and detritus of all description. In the process of avoiding everything around you it is almost impossible to stay upright. I can imagine that continually traversing these streets day in, day out, at this rate of psychic intensity, could be the end of you. The three of us walk back through Chinatown to Amsterdam Centraal. Avoiding the clusters of pimps and dealers who guard the station's entrances like the Watchers at Mordor's gate, we get to the platform for the night train and stare out over this stately nineteenth-century structure which, framed by its majestic arching glass roof, resembles nothing so much as a vast, Piranesian detention centre for the drunk. I am tired and suffering from a beer headache, so I slump on a bench and wait.

When it arrives the train is full of screeching and lowing provincial lunatics. Nearing Leiden I am given what I take to be an aspirin by Middlesbrough #1, who suggests hitting a bar or two and maybe a party where someone will play records before I can catch the first bus back to the Bollenstreek. What else am I to do? After about ten minutes I realize that the aspirin was actually some form of recreational drug, ingested, to cap it all, in the small hours of Queen Beatrix's official birthday.

Beyond all help, I am exploring the radiations emanating from my arms on the tiny dancefloor of Leiden's Jazzmatazz club, while around me a confrontation between a bunch of lads who make the pizzas in one of the many small Italian restaurants in town and some local gangster types turns heavy. I, however, am uninterested in all manifestations of violence, revelling in the fact that all the answers I need in my life are on the tip of my tongue, if only I could trigger that first question. I'm grabbed by someone familiar: it's the girl at work who ran away from her Christian sect. We leave to find the party Middlesbrough #1 mentioned, avoiding the flying glass.

We go down a quiet side street behind the imposing Lido cinema, knock on a door and are ushered in. An insect-like man is playing records. People sit in various states of disarray nodding along to the ambient post-rave soundtrack. There is a bar of sorts. I am increasingly strident, revelling in this magnificent state of all-knowing. It may be past four o'clock in the morning but the world is displayed before me like a Rubens canvas and I demand another aspirin. The Middlesbrough lads have left though, and the Christian Girl does a good job of talking some sense into me. After maybe an hour of wondering how to explain the beauty of the world to anyone who wants to listen, and experiencing an increasing melancholy like the Mock Turtle, I plot my next move.

I could walk down to the nearby Rembrandt cafe, a very Dutch institution that serves bottles of beer in the early morning to postmen, those addicted to the unofficial national sport of carp fishing and the peculiar band of morose middle-aged men whose wives and partners have thrown them out of the house. I decide against this. A *shoarma* place, as ever, is open. Eating food in a licensed public place between the hours of three and six o'clock in the morning is one of the great markers of a civilized country. And Leiden is a civilized city, with its numerous *shoarma* joints, each displaying some form of hand-painted mural of a desert oasis and a television showing the latest pop-music videos, all of which involve painful-looking gyrations masquerading as dance moves. None seem to close until the last customer leaves: another advantage. The regular crowd in this and other *shoarma* joints consists of pasty-faced male students, professional loners and people who like to shout at windows. The trick is to buy a *schotel* (a plate of *shoarma* and pitta bread with chips and a salad), eat some, sleep a bit next to it, wake up, eat some more and watch the clock tick by as you wait for your means of public conveyance.

After this rite is carried out to the satisfaction of all parties, I walk to Leiden Centraal and wait in the station cafe surrounded by frowning pairs of Dutch ladies dressed in hiking gear. They have maps and guidebooks spread out on the tables in front of them. Where on earth are they going at this hour? They are probably thinking the same of me. I bump into a red-eyed lad from Sunderland and his mate who are also heading towards the coast. In a high state of excitement and repeating himself regularly, Mr Sunderland tells us all about his grandfather, who would walk six miles to work and back every day. This really is the ultimate Imperial British working-class fantasy, played out as a frazzled call to class solidarity amongst us factory hands.

The bus comes. I alight at Noordwijkerhout, buy some yoghurt and buttermilk at the campsite shop, crash onto my unmade bed and spend the next eighteen hours asleep.

RADIO HORRORS: AN INTRODUCTION

A DART NARROWLY MISSES ME as I enter the elevated Portakabin that my supervisor and his right-hand man inhabit, and firmly wedges itself into a picture of the face of Slobodan Milošević. Both lads are from Kosovo, a name much in the news recently. They're building their lives in a new country but like to remember old friends when they can.

'Can we switch the radio station?'

'No.'

Another dart thuds into the old president's forehead.

'Don't ask again! We're too busy at the moment.'

I trudge back down the metal stairs and hear Carlos Santana and the Product G&B's 'Maria Maria' for the third or maybe fourth time today. And it's overtime tonight, which means we will get an extra helping or two of this particular sonic treat.

I have been here just over a month now but I know my real enemy. Creating an ambience of its own, cutting through our factory days and informing our moods and actions, is the sound of Dutch commercial radio. There are a number of stations to choose from. Now and again we switch over when the limited playlist on one station gets too much, only to switch back to a couple of staples when the others become unbearable. Regardless, each one broadcasts its own peculiar brand of chirruping, dayglo awfulness. These broadcasters have short, catchy names, there to impart the feel that the modern world is exciting and you'd better get on board, Daddy-O. Also the presenters are, without exception, male. Relentlessly upbeat and friendly, these lads share an amusing trick of deepening the timbre of their voices when about to say something important or play a track they obviously like. They also indulge in a lot of laughing.

The station we listen to most has a number for a name. It really has the hots for Carlos Santana and the Product G&B's 'Maria Maria'. I get to my table and, starting to staple empty boxes for an order, ponder how I came to loathe listening to the radio.

During my first week, still in a bubble of wonder at finding myself living and working full time in a different country, I didn't notice anything much apart from the general ambience created by the light, percussive pop and sparkly house music. Positive stuff, and none of the chest-beating aggrandizement of British pop radio. I have since noticed the rotation of many old songs that I haven't heard in years: songs my doleful teenage self would have seen as the gold standard of 1980s awfulness, purveyors of soul-boy schmaltz or the epitome of chrome-kissed, unattainable Thatcherite–Reaganite dreams. Initially I thought, 'Wow, these Dutch are smart, with their hilarious and subtle put down of the mores of 1980s chart-music shows. Mainland Europeans really are cut from a superior cultural cloth.' It has since dawned on me that both the audience, if my Dutch colleagues are anything to go by, and presenters really, really like listening to such artists as Phil Collins's Genesis, Céline Dion, Bryan Adams, Queen, Wham!, the Rolling Stones, Level 42 (a particular favourite it seems, but why?), Chris de Burgh and Paul Young.

Littered amongst the works of these artists come other moments of long-forgotten torture which still manage to give out momentary, surgical stabs of pain: Yes with 'Owner of a Lonely Heart', a Colonel Abrams twelve-inch remix, or Rick Astley's groanathon 'Together Forever'. Then, occasionally surfacing from a more concentrated circle of aural hell, Nik Kershaw and his abominable lullaby 'The Riddle', which seems to be held up as a work of philosophical genius by some presenters, T'Pau's operatic death scream 'China in Your Hand' and Cutting Crew's execrable yodel 'I Just Died in Your Arms Tonight'. It never stops.

One day, a fortnight or so into my time here, and wearied by another punctured-balloon whine from Nik Kershaw, I asked Kasper: 'Why do they play so many old songs on the radio?'

'They don't play that many old songs.'

'Ach, come on, they're playing Nik Kershaw! It's from 1983! What do you like, Kasper? You can't like this stuff, surely?'

Kasper huffily turned away. 'They're good tunes. I don't think about music like that. I like some rock. Take it easy!'

Somehow I had crossed an invisible line. My first mistake. To criticize music radio is to criticize a widely accepted cog in the working patterns of Dutch socio-economic life. Radio is my first real window into the Dutch soul and I have found it wanting. It's not reflective of an imagined nation of philosopher kings like Johan Cruyff that I'd naively thought it was. But to talk about the music played on the radio here in any way, especially in a critical or sociocultural way, seems to make a number of my Dutch colleagues uneasy.

Soon after my mild baiting of Kasper I found myself crawling around on all fours under the iron roof supports, cleaning out the dusty shipping cartons in the nethermost reaches of the scaffolding lining the factory walls.

A pallet of boxes finished, I grab another and start on another size of box, one for apple-tree saplings. These boxes are long and pretty squat. You have to make sure they are stapled just right, otherwise they are slightly out of shape and difficult to stack. But I'm pretty good at this, and I can time my stapling to the rhythm of No Doubt's 'Don't Speak' in an attempt to block the work and the song from my mind simultaneously. Yes, these radio dudes do modern, too. We are reminded daily that we are living in a spring heralding a new millennium with current tracks from Pink, Eminem, Jennifer Lopez, the aforementioned Carlos Santana and the loveable Britney Spears. Eiffel 65's 'Blue' is everywhere. Its nonsensical 'Downtown Nyoo Yoikk' mumbling rap monologue somehow becomes the unguent that greases the conveyor rails we push the finished orders down. Irritating eardrum piercings are delivered at regular intervals courtesy of Shania Twain and Anastacia, and a mildly catatonic state is brought about by the much-hated Dido and her schoolgirl-diary take on pop. Bon Jovi comes back to haunt us like a mildly drunken uncle with 'It's My Life'. Young tracksuit prince Craig David tells us all how to make love in this carefree time of plenty with '7 Days', while Robbie Williams presides over this shrink-wrapped CD Tower of Babel as the Joker King. Every day.

It is also very noticeable how little Dutch music there is in the day-time schedules. Golden Earring get regular airplay with their rousing 1970s rockers 'Radar Love' and 'Twilight Zone'. Both are very enjoyable, up-tempo numbers blessed with real nous, somehow sidestepping the lumpy attempts at wanting to be players in the 'international pop world' their compatriots seem to suffer from. There is a strong streak of sermonizing melancholy in Dutch pop which begins to irritate over time. The Nits often get an airing with 'In the Dutch Mountains', which is as plodding a slice of misdirected nonsense as you could wish for. And the less said about Marco Borsato's stool-straining 'Binnen' ('Inside') the better.

Then there is Anouk, a young, blonde Dutchwoman who sounds feisty enough with her snarling rockers 'R U Kiddin' Me' and 'Nobody's Wife'. Both are pretty enjoyable the first time you hear them each day, and still just about bearable by the fifth. Anouk is a Dutch take on the 'tough girl with guts' international pop trope. This role usually demands a 'tell-all ballad' at some point in the career trajectory, and Anouk's latest single 'Michel' ticks all the boxes. In the unrelieved, grindingly slow intensity of its despair, not to mention its open wound, death-wish soul-searching, 'Michel' is highly inappropriate musical fare for a factory trying to pack thousands of orders a day. The Brabantse band Krezip and Frisian duo Twarres both give variations on this style with limp ballads called 'I Would Stay' and 'Wêr Bisto' ('Where Are You'), songs I begin to time my toilet breaks to. The latest Dutch rock sound is represented by the slick bombast of Kane, whose singer continually sounds like he's running to catch a bus. Most played of all in this spring of 2000 is Vlissingen's BLØF and their paean to the Zeeland coastline 'Aan de Kust' ('On the Coast'). This dirge, like all of BLØF's songs, manages to sound like a middle-aged man moaning about the football in an empty bar.

I pause mid-order. Maybe I have the answer to why this 'radio experience' is the way it is. In the world of Netherlands commercial radio, popular music is there as a means to invoke a vague content-edness with the way of the world, a *savoir faire* at one remove, born of knowing solely what is popular and successful. Continual playlist repetitions are there to create a cosy sense of familiarity, solidarity with your workmates, and a sharing of the emotions of that day's broadcast. In real, floor-time terms, resistance is useless. For the precocious wallflowers amongst us, listening to this kind of music repetitively, without recourse to anything else, over time breeds a weary, Nabokovian acceptance of the underlying, structural shitness of life. Micro counter aggressions are the only resistance. Adopting the rhythm of a track into the biomechanics of your own work is one way to bear its load. You can treat the bumps and grinds of a Kane song as the thumps and wriggles of an annoying toddler that you have to carry on your back. There again you can throw a gnomic, sarcastic aside to some utopian banality squeezed out by Freddie Mercury, or grit your teeth and go double fast through Bon Jovi to show the old goat that he won't beat you in stickering 250 rose boxes. That kind of thing. Day by day. Or, like many of my colleagues, you can take drugs.

The other thing commercial radio is known for are the jingles. Normally these happen when midday or a new show approaches, which often correlate with a break for us. So we welcome it when the commercials start up. We know we are all one step closer to a coffee. Still, Dutch adverts are weird. They often use an English tagline. One pizza-delivery company couples the line 'Lekker thuis uit eten!' ('Eat out at home!') with 'Now you're talking!' Doubtless the pizza lads thought they could win hearts and minds with an inviting call to action but the slogan misses by miles with its fruity, church-hall tone. Not that it matters to Dutch ears. It's an English phrase, which seals the deal. There is also a lesson here, quickly learned, in how a language with all its attendant nuances, power structures and histories can be put to task in a way that is utterly alien to how native speakers understand things. This lingual interzone is also seen with the garbled English phrases that are stitched or transferred onto the T-shirts and sweatshirts of my Dutch colleagues. Utter nonsense like 'Out There Dog', 'Digging the Groove' or 'Love Me in the Sun' is worn without a semblance of embarrassment or even cognizance by disconsolate-looking, paunchy men dropping off stacks of pallets.

Some adverts use English in a manner that is eye-wateringly racist and sexist. One, promoting holiday insurance, creates a scenario involving a party of Dutch tourists stranded somewhere in Africa. The tourists are dealing with a bent holiday rep-cum-kidnapper with a 'scary-baddy African' voice, replete with a deep, evil laugh. Every time I hear it I wonder what mental or emotional world the makers of these adverts live in, doubtless sat round some polished chrome and glass table outside Amsterdam.

I stop philosophizing about Dutch radio and wider forms of linguistics as my Kosovan supervisor calls me over. He's one for regularly telling people why he's made a decision, as if to salve his own conscience. He's from a land with a rich musical tradition after all; surely he knows how dispiriting repetitive playlists can be.

'We're not going to change the radio because some of the regulars like it. But here's the deal. Tonight we are doing overtime until nine o'clock. And then it's down to you and your mates to choose. You can work to whatever you like, and have it on loud, too.'

He makes this sound like a pay rise. He's happy: problem solved. Except it's still not really solving anything.

It's seven o'clock and we trudge back towards the factory floor from the canteen, our insides cemented with a large portion of shoarma, chips and mayonnaise. One of us, not me, has gone to switch the radio channel. Not that it really matters as the music will alter but follow the same broad pattern across stations. It just depends what level of intensity you are after. Overtime is normally when we hear dance music, specifically happy hardcore. These are the sounds that the stations perceive as examples of contemporary club culture, and there to show the Dutch as the legitimate, nonstop party animals in a European dayglo neverland. The male presenter voices drop an octave to reflect this status as we head into the night and listen to more 'serious', 'world-beating' music.

I pick up my airgun and start working to the rhythm of these simple, interchangeable but highly effective dance tracks. They are usually built around a female voice that sounds like it's ingested a bucket's worth of helium. This girl plaintively sings of the various magical places she'd like to take you to, normally paradisiacal glades on the greensward that boast a bridge or tree of some mystical significance, where you can find a dragon or wise teacher. I flip a flatpack box into shape and shoot two staples into its bottom, keeping some kind of time to the *doof doof*. All the while I wait for the drop. How many boxes can I make before the pummelling relents?

Here we go, it's going quiet, and I've got eight large boxes for climbing roses done; enough to stack as a layer on the pallet next to me. The inevitable drops in the music are introduced by some thoughtful piano coda that mutates the track into a dreamscape. Then comes a synthesized flute sound, conjuring a primary-coloured Arcady forever lit by the rainbow's glow, populated by tattooed nymphs and shaven-headed satyrs with bulging muscles. I line my stapled boxes up on my table and toss the instructions and soil blocks in. The point where dancing can start again is heralded by the reintroduction of the beat, sounding like a hyper-sped-up version of someone running on the spot, or using a power drill in a neighbouring flat. The Chipmunk-as-Rusalka harmonics return, only to dissolve then reappear, like shifting sugar mountains. Time to stick the roses in.

I was moaning to myself about the radio earlier but it's actually OK music to work to. It's obviously inane and made for gurning teens on sulphates but, as with a number of supposedly nonsensical music forms, this sort of dance music trails unexpected clouds of glory. Like this thing we are all working to now, an old Madonna track pressed into action, the original hooks chopped up like offal and thrown into a spitting, fizzing blender, only to re-emerge as a pummelled mush of nothingness. We factory hands, full of coffee, shoarma, chips and mayonnaise, subliminally take in the message that everything's gonna be all right.

*

The next day, knowing there will be another bout of overtime, I decide to do something different on my lunch break just to shake things up a bit. Next to the factory is a big garden centre, a sprawling complex that sells a lot of unrelated things like tea towels and marked-down Easter and Christmas decorations. The Dutch love their gardens and bargains. They also like walking at unimaginably slow speeds through the centre, inspecting everything, or rather gazing at a range of items, picking some up, raising their eyebrows at the price and then putting them back. I'm not here for anthropological reasons, though. In the middle of the complex, decorated like some remote bush station amongst the potted ferns, is a cafe that sells hot food including soups and toasted sandwiches and, most enticingly, the Dutch version of the sausage roll, the saucijzenbroodje. I am all too aware that to enjoy this snack in situ means running the risk of hearing a Céline Dion number. Céline Dion is popular in the Netherlands. To me, the genius of Dion's music seems to be located in the way that her incredible vocal exertions, only matched on the parade ground at Sandhurst or an Alpine mountainside when a shepherd calls in a flock of goats, can be employed to reassure masses of solid Dutch citizens that moving at a snail's pace around this garden centre is the pinnacle of their day.

Sitting in a bamboo chair at a glass-topped bamboo table, I munch on my salty, greasy snack and slurp my filter coffee with great satisfaction. My German army shirt and boots and grimy jeans do not sit well with those around me. I get the odd disapproving look from the elderly clientele. But this is of no matter, for here, in the garden centre, amongst the lush vegetation, Dion's caterwauling desensitizes everything and everyone. Those taking their teeth out to masticate their apple pie, the mousey looking men with lists and spades and the red-faced, long-lost grandsons of Otto von Bismarck who buy trellising and weedkiller. Or even the stately Dutch housewives, with their short-cropped, red-rinsed Jimmy Somerville hairdos and sweatshirt-and-trouser combos, and those of a more arty persuasion who sport white spandex leggings underneath a flowing ethnic dress set off with wooden beads. They sail like galleons through the foliage, humming Dion's numbers, unconsciously revelling in their banal agencies, unwittingly conspiring in the music's role as a memory wipe: celebrating the fact that these ridiculous vocal gymnastics act as the epitome of 'taking it easy' without ever having to explain why.

INTERLUDE: BULB FIELDS

MID-MAY. The nights lengthen and the cycle home after overtime is no longer in the dark. This fact is a real spirit-lifter, and one that allows another balm to take full hold.

Cycling home after another late shift to make up for the days we lost the previous week because of *Bevrijdingsdag* on 5 May, I look at the fields around me and think about how quickly the seasons move on here. Right now I'm passing wave after wave of tulips planted in rows in the fields. It's a beautiful experience, one that leavens the schlep of factory life. Each strip is a bright, shimmering contrast to the intervening strips of grey-brown sandy land.

I realize they won't be here for long, which makes my fleeting interactions with them all the more precious. My early, lonely days working here were made bearable by gazing out over the hyacinth fields displaying thousands of blue, pink, purple, deep-red, white and yellow flowers. First experienced in the sharp, changeable days of April, the heady aroma given off by these stocky, bulbous perfume machines was an overwhelming experience. The waves of scent blown into my face by the constant spring gusts created a sensation of being lifted metres from the ground.

Alongside them were the fields of narcissi, which announced themselves in flashes of yellow or creamy white. Sometimes you could catch their organic compound indole smell on the breeze, which can be very sharp: a reminder that these wan, delicate-looking plants were very much alive and reflecting the water and sand and fertilizers they stood in. Nearby were the fields of crocuses, normally purple, yellow or white, adding a silent, secret note, their flowers so small and fragile-looking it often felt as if they wouldn't survive the night.

And just in time for the first drawing out of the days in late April and early May came the tulips. They are at their zenith now in the first weeks of May. Turning off the Lisse road northwards towards Noordwijkerhout, and cycling past seemingly endless rows of them, I make a mental note of the tulip types I have seen and can recognize. I remember the small botanical varieties, more like wildflowers and far too wayward to be organized in rows. Others, more compact, such as Praestans Fusilier, a small, compact plant with a blazing red flower and a rich viridian leaf, hug the ground and form thick lines of unbroken colour. Then there are the taller 'classic' varieties, the ones the tourists really come to see. Looking out over these massed ranks of tulips, even when on my bike, is like passing into a bucolic, slightly psychedelic world that is parallel to the everyday. When planted together in blocks of contrasting colour, the fields start to look like the old test cards from the early days of colour television. And on a clear sunny evening like this one the rows of plants resemble a mirage, something unreal, lavish slabs of oil paint on a palette that start to radiate in front of me. There is a constant ripple of movement; the optics are illusionary, somehow suggestive of great depth and a formidable press of vegetation. But if I just get off my bike and get down to the level of the bulbs, or walk in a fallow, sandy row between each press of plants, this feeling of power and solidity will instantly recede into mere rows of regularly planted flowers. There is always the feeling that you will never unlock the secret to the real beauty of a tulip field in full bloom; forget trying to photograph or paint them, it's a waste of time trying to capture what you really saw.

I think of the main road into Lisse just in front of my factory, where there is a layby. Here, coachloads of tourists step out for five minutes to photograph the fields on their way to the Keukenhof. They are served by a rudimentary wooden stall standing open to the elements, where bags of bulbs can be bought. It is normally manned by a grumpy local who looks like he's dressed up specially as a mud-stained bulb worker. Although probably not: I would bet he just can't be bothered to change his clothes. The only thing that interests him is selling the bags of flowers to the misguided romantics amongst these day trippers. In the main the tourists are German, coming in from the Ruhr or Rhineland, but there are a fair number of Japanese and Americans amongst them. It's sometimes difficult not to laugh at the tourists gawping, but seeing so many people taking so much open delight in flowers, couples hugging on a field's edge and others trying, tentatively, to get as close as they can to these delicate rows of plants, is disarming. If only they'd get off the bloody cycle path.

I'm nearly home. Ach, it's a lovely night, I'll take the backwoods path and avoid the caravan for another fifteen minutes.

I bear left, taking the small road bypassing the village and swing left again, along a tree-lined side road. This leads me to a pleasant area overlooking one of the many backroads field complexes, not on any tourist route. Not expecting to see anyone, I snap out of my reverie as I narrowly miss crashing into a lone Japanese lad wearing a bucket hat, his long hair in a ponytail. He's busy serenading a field full of tall pink tulips with a wooden recorder, and swaying slightly to the notes he's picking out on his instrument. Maybe the scene in front of him has put him in a trance-like state. Maybe he's offering a devotional, an act of totemism on the fly. More perturbations ensue when I look closely at him and note he bears a remarkable resemblance to Damo Suzuki, lead singer of the 1970s German rock group Can. It can't be him, of course, but maybe it's his son. And it's just the sort of thing Damo would do. I cycle on.

THE VILLAGE PUB

MY NEW TEMPORARY FRIEND is a thickset, close-cropped Polish lad, one of an increasing number of Polish workers on the campsite. He's sleeping in the caravan next to me, and is very keen to know where he can get a drink. As it's a Friday afternoon and we've both just finished work, it's not an unreasonable suggestion. I suggest a local pub. He wants to go as soon as possible.

The pub is situated in the village of Noordwijkerhout. This means a twenty-minute trek through the backroads past campsites, farms, riding stables and the strange, ultra-neat, ultra-kitsch front gardens the Dutch seem to love. It is still a wonder to me why Dutch gardens all look the same, and why no one has come to blows about this fact. Our walk is conducted at an ever-increasing pace, and conversation is kept to a brisk minimum. My Polish pal is obviously looking forward to slaking his thirst. I'm looking forward to having a night of fun with my friends, in the pub I feel most at home in.

There are a number of pubs to frequent in Noordwijkerhout, and like pubs, cafes and bars around the world, each attracts its own specific clientele. The one we are heading to is well known as a hangout for local foreign workers and the more internationally minded of the Dutch villagers. It's called De Schotse Bar, aka the Scots Bar. I like it a lot, it's a laugh. The entrance of De Schotse Bar is unremarkable enough, opening onto a long, narrow room that can just about accommodate a circular table near the street-facing window. First impressions are that of a front parlour, beach hut and boozer all in one. Wildly diverse pictures, flags, nick-nacks and other nameless paraphernalia that make up the decor add to the confusion. De Schotse Bar is also a strange place as far as the light goes. Sometimes the sunlight can blaze in; at other times it's the smoky epitome of a Dutch *bruin café*. These changes in the light and the bar's narrowness add to a feeling there is an indigenous ecosystem here that has developed over time: an atmosphere known only to initiates and something that adds to a decidedly surreal air when the witching hour approaches. When that hour comes, the place turns, as if by magic, into a dayglo fairy disco with a substratum of deranged hedonism.

The wreckhead feeling is supported by hundreds of photos of clients getting mashed up on previous nights. They plaster the walls. Sun-bleached, beer-stained, fingerprinted, curling and greasy; grins, gurns, rolling eyes, open mouths, flailing limbs and menacing stares; in costume, in work gear and dressed up outrageously for the Lent carnival; all frozen, all silent, all helpless; the pictures stare back as silent witnesses. This is the club you can join if you drink regularly enough to be accepted here.

At the opposite end of the bar are the jakes and a cramped space that can be used as a dancefloor. The toilets are normally in use for some purpose or other. There's also a small patio-cum-beer garden in the back, looking over a bit of the street and a plot of undeveloped land behind the road that leads to Haarlem. I have noticed that this is the place where on warmer nights a certain crowd gathers, members of which come in with spittle around the mouth needing a beer, only to disappear again, howling and jabbering.

It's Friday night so things are starting early. For many who nod to us as we walk in, the evening's entertainment starts as a pitstop on the way home from work and may carry on until the next day, if so desired. I'm starving, it must be said. The bar provides pie and beans for those who fancy dining out, the choice normally being cheese and onion or beef and potato, or whatever has come in from the latest run home. Beans come in one variety: from the shop. Beer glasses are available in the usual shapes, namely *fluitje*, *vaasje*, *halve liter* and, maybe as a sign of the bar's international flavour, pint barrel glasses with handles. Like many others, however, I have got used to drinking beer from 33 cl bottles, especially the brand Hertog Jan. The bottle proudly displays a label showing a ruddy-faced, noble chap in ermine with a crown on his head. Hertog is one of the few independent beers to be found in the country. It's worth coughing up the extra twenty-five guldercents for. Plus the bottles are easier to carry around, lessening the chance of a spiked or spilt beverage.

I order my bottle of Hertog and a pie while my new Polish friend gets a pint, downs it in one gulp and gets another, visibly calmed. I lose him almost instantly to a small press of unsmiling Polish lads dressed like lumberjacks who are about to move next door to a joint with an oblong bar called Madeiro. Madeiro gives off a weird vibe somewhere between cosy *bruin café* and wannabe gangster den. I can't say I ever really enjoy sitting in there, even though the people are friendly enough: it's as if everyone is waiting for a signal to do a job. No worries, there are plenty of other workmates or regulars from other factories. I settle down to eat my pie.

Not long after, my pal the Welsh Poet walks in. Soundtracked by the infantile melody and strength-sapping beat of Wamdue Project's smash hit 'King of My Castle', we fall into talking about Robert Graves, Offa's Dyke and what we will do with our holiday stamps. His girlfriend, an instantly likeable and very loud Irish lass with flaming copper-red hair and someone who is forever in high spirits, is also telling me about the old Birmingham heavy-rock band Black Sabbath, mostly about how she fucking loves them. This is a tale of love that, if the current stream of enthusiasm is kept up, can last a night's telling. She asks the bar staff to play Black Sabbath. They do: 'Paranoid'. She screams and wails along to it in her high-pitched voice. There are a few things I've learned about my colleagues in my relatively short time working in the bulbs. One is that an awful lot of people who live in the caravan parks and squats really like Black Sabbath and the American thrash band Slayer. None seem to have the outward appearance of heavy-metal fans. Maybe it's something in the pagan, daredevil proclivities of both acts.

Applying a local sociocultural patina to this love of heavy rock and metal is not something I or the Welsh Poet can muse on for long: a revolving cast of partyheads pass regularly by. Some we know, others are new. One new lad looks hard as nails. Shaven-headed, Pre-Raphaelite in profile and with a mad glint in his cornflower-blue eyes, he settles unannounced next to us and starts to talk. The whites of his eyes are pronounced, as is the spider tattoo on his neck. He's a Londoner. He gets straight to the point.

'Do you know anywhere to sleep? And no, before you ask, I don't mean in your fucking caravan. I need something better than that.'

I tell him I don't know anywhere.

'Oh well, I'm looking for somewhere like the Slobs used to be.'

I look dumbly on.

'Wet, are you? Clever boy, are you? You seem it. It was a place in Haarlem a few years back. I got in there by using a crowbar. Never mind, sweetie, I'll scout about. The thing to do is look around for a few weeks, wait, and then get down there with a set of cutters, a crowbar and some tools. Take some dry food too. Then you have to board the place up quick to stop the police. Then sort the water. Why are you looking at my tattoo? Got that done in Brighton years back. Like it, do you? Like to look, do you? Want to see more?' It's dawning on me that I am maybe one misplaced remark away from agreeing to some esoteric sexual practice.

Luckily things are hotting up and, although it's just past seven o'clock in the evening, the place is soon a shifting, blazing ectoplasm of all sexes and sizes. Both my interrogator and I are talking to others very quickly. I get grabbed by the two Irish girls who share a caravan on the campsite. The Ulster one is apologizing to me for temporarily losing my bike on a recent trip to the shops. She's also laughing loudly at me for being so gullible as to lend it to her in the first place.

'Surely you knew I wouldn't come back with it?' It nearly went the way of the other things I've loaned out. Two books on archaeology and Robert Graves's *The White Goddess* are now probably three or four pairs of hands down the line, doubtless in exchange for some substance or other.

'Hang on a mo.' She grabs a pen from the bar's owner and writes something on a piece of paper, folds it up and passes it to me. It says: 'You wee dafty.' I'll take that.

Some people are moving on after boozing up in here since the place opened just after midday. My mate An Garda Síochána is off to his flat for a lie-down in front of the telly, flushed and singing about what he's going to do with his holiday stamps. His work season is finished.

Laughing, he tells me why he's staying in the Netherlands. 'I spoke to my parents. They said, "What are you up to this summer, son?", and I told them I'd already been round all the churches and museums with you, my new clever English friend. And that I was going to get reading again and get back into education. "Ah," they said, "don't lie, we know you, we know what you'll be up to! Drinking! English friends? Sitting around all day, more like!" No point going back to that, is there?'

No, I agree, probably not. A trio of Irish lads from Belfast join us. One is a genial soul who has something of Dean Martin about him. We talk of why the Golden Mile is the best drinking run in all of the island group. He wants to go back, but not just yet. Another wears an Arsenal shirt and is constantly looking for a rise from me. Thing is I like him as he's often a funny and generous lad, so I won't take the bait, even if I feel compelled to. He has a nervous tick which worsens when he gets agitated. Twitching and sweating in front of me, he starts on a random spiel about the English: a set of jumbled observations from clothing to football and dogs to guns that have little to do with me. I stand mute. None of it makes sense.

The third, who looks like a professor, takes up the baton. 'You English, you never understand, do you? Ireland is an occupied country. You are an occupying force. You're not a bad guy personally but you're all so bloody arrogant on one level. English people don't care that we even exist.' He turns to nod to an older tattooed lad with swept-back hair, a West Countryman who has previously told me he was in the Royal Green Jackets. He's an amiable charmer who nobody would want to get on the wrong side of, and he compliments me on my desert boots.

'Got them at the Legerdump in Leiden, did yer?' I tell him I did. 'Good man. They sell some proper waterproof capes down there, too. Ones you could use as a groundsheet and a tent if you got stuck out in the open. All you really need is a good knife, some flint to start a fire, a decent water bottle and some dubbin and you could get out and survive.'

Before I have time to process what is going on, a group of English and Dutch join the outer circle, talking loudly about having just got back from Thailand.

The Welsh Poet wrinkles his nose, signalling a certain weariness. 'That lot. I bet they'll boast about the orgy they claimed they went to out there. Or the time they were having sex with locals on the beaches. Or how they got out of it in Denmark.' It's not that he disapproves of the subject matter, rather that he's sick of hearing the same, reheated stories. Nothing is off limits in the telling, here in the Netherlands, outside of repeating old tropes. Everyone is trying out a new reality to some degree, away from the stresses of their home countries. Escaping the monarchy, the theocracy, the law, poverty, boredom, sexual intimidation or the aftermath of various peace processes. Stories are swapped, some verifiable, some surely imaginary, all adding to the carousel of myth and hearsay that drives the news for these international temporary workers. But being boring about things is a no-no.

Time for another drink. The bar is run by a tall, commanding lady who has obviously seen everything in her time. I'm all right in here because she likes me. Her second in command is a friendly and funny Liverpool girl who's much too quick-witted for the likes of me. They are both laughing at me for getting it in the neck from all sides. I get given a beer. Then, as if working to a secret and silent command, they swing into action and turn the music up. Things are changing yet again.

A number of thirty-something locals are drifting in. I have spoken to this bunch before and they are friendly enough: partyheads who favour floral shirts and spangly leggings, or squatter hippy attire with plenty of floaty Palestinian-style scarves, or tracksuits. This lot also seem to have recourse to an endless supply of sunglasses. They throw strained, manic grins in our direction and head out to the beer garden. Immediately following them are other men, ones with very prominent tattoos and smiles like the flat of a knife. I know that these lads are best avoided.

I look around and spot one or two of the other Dutch regulars propped up at the end of the bar, members of a small, disparate group of single men of middle age who seem to have been adopted as father figures by many in the pub. Some live in a big open-plan complex on the other side of the village that deals with a range of psychiatric patients. They like drinking with all of us, and we like seeing them here. One of them looks very much like Van Gogh. He has a very odd pair of almost schoolboy shorts on. A friend of mine at the factory who lives in the village told me about him. 'He always tells me, "I can lick you like Lassie the dog!"' It's a sign of endearment. Apparently, one of the bar staff cuts his hair in here, when there's a quiet moment. Next to him is a big bear of a guy with striking white hair. He's a lovely, mild-mannered man of tremendous strength, who has been rumoured to destroy pool balls by squeezing them.

As the evening progresses the bar's fittings start to warp and move, the muggy, charged atmosphere bringing them to life. The lighting, warm and bright, almost sickly, starts to play tricks: the faces from the photographs start to melt into the those of the living, creating a bacchanalian tapestry akin to some miniature of a demented peasants' feast. A picture of a jolly Dutch miller smiles maniacally across from one wall, giving unction to the piss-up. Various locals mingling outside come in yodelling some nonsense or other and grin uncomprehendingly over at us, unsure as to who we are. Some clearly fail to recognize us, despite them saying hello earlier. I can understand that the revolving cast of *Engels en Ierse* must be difficult to keep track of. 'I need Snow! Argh! Haha!'

A local girl of this group, one who also travels around the sites with her Scottish boyfriend selling pills, tells me that the owner of my campsite was found in flagrante in the showers with a Polish cleaner girl, and that some biker lad hanged his dog on another campsite. More grist for the rumour mill. Another Dutch friend sidles over from outside. He's a gentle sort who wants to connect with nature and sleeps on a wooden export pallet in the back bedroom of a house in the village. Now he's bug-eyed, roaring nonsense and demanding we talk about books to him to calm him down. He lets on that he's not sure how things will pan out with him and his landlord, who, like many locals, isn't totally sure that they are doing the right thing in letting hippy barbarians lower the tone of the village. Especially a Dutchman who is inexplicably adopting the code of the *buitenlanders*.

More car parties turn up outside, offloading further grinning, be-sunglassed types. Some of these characters are shaven-headed man mountains with prominent Ajax tattoos covering bare arms. Despite their size these leviathans bray for a *fluitje*, the smallest glass on offer. Their beers look microscopic in their hands, like the floats attached to fishing rods.

Somebody behind the bar turns the music up; it's Moby, whose LP *Play* seems to invade every public space. This spring the race for our ears is generally between Moby and something execrable by Robbie Williams. No matter: the sort of music snobbery you can indulge in back in Blighty is unheard of or totally dismissed amongst these peripatetic tribes. Fun, in whatever form, has to be seized. There is an attempt at dancing in the small space near the permanently engaged jakes and, as if in answer, a number of football chants and old folk and rebel songs get blasted out a cappella at the other end of the bar. The people singing these are hanging on to each other regardless of outward allegiance, or sprawled and slumped against the bar at odd angles, unwittingly adopting the survivor poses from *The Raft of the Medusa*. Looking out over everything, the De Schotse Bar staff preside over this flotsam of cultures and histories, washing up against each other like the discoloured foam from the nearby beaches.

Somehow it's three o'clock in the morning. It feels like we've all been shrunk and placed inside a brightly coloured balloon that is difficult to get out of. Human *scènes des naufrages* are all around me. Trying to steady myself, realizing I still need to shower after work, and that at some point today I have to get food in for the following week, I decide to leave. The trek back to the campsite, despite being on a relatively secluded road, doesn't feel safe, as I am sure the party cars and lone cyclists who career past me now and again aren't as gimlet-eyed as I would like them to be.

I walk into the campsite and, amongst the odd shriek and gibber emanating from some of the more spaced-out inhabitants, I hear a nightingale in the nearby woods. It's the only time I've heard one so late; normally they like to sing in the heat of noon. Amplified by the relative stillness of the night, its rich, extraordinary sound cascades over the field, at once impossible to mistake and impossible to describe, like a broadcast from another world.

*

Saturday morning may be heralded by an ugly hangover but it demands action in the form of stocking up, so I pop into the village. I negotiate the uncomfortable experience of shopping in the main supermarket, where the thrill of buying things I have never heard of continues. I buy packs of my favourite staple stodge, *ontbijtkoek*. The dizzying variety of cooked and cured meats and attendant sauces makes me wonder whether all of mainland Europe's ingenuity has been directed solely at carving up pigs. As always, the *kasa* girl doesn't smile or even look up when I pay. Neither do the people behind the counter in the specialist cheese shop I like to treat myself in. Doing normal things normally, like the locals, never seems to get me anywhere in Noordwijkerhout.

I take the opportunity to visit a bar for a pick-me-up and chinwag. It's either that or go back and add to the general air of moping indolence on the campsite. There are a number of choices: one is Feest Van Harry, aka Harry's Bar. It's a place where the enjoyment levels are entirely dependent on who's in. It's what the Dutch call a 'party tent': every aspect is set out to please, with nice round tables and a well-appointed and clean interior. Nevertheless the perennial party mood here feels *soi-disant*. Harry's Bar has the feel of a place where local happiness and contentment with the workings of the Dutch state are put on display at all opportunities, and whatever you bring to the atmosphere has to chime with this overriding concern. Still, it's a nice place to grab a coffee and look over the square and white church that are the focal points of the village.

Café Van Der Geest, where I am heading, is another matter. This is a roomy but inviting cafe and serves as a talking shop for many: a place where a certain pretence to civilization and local tradition (at least in Dutch eyes) is upheld. A staircase on the side of the building leads to an extension which serves as a mini hotel where a number of people I work with are staying. Inside, the wooden panelling, comfy seating and polished brass fittings hint at pretensions of a grand cafe in the wider European mould. There is a luxurious pool table and a set of function rooms, on the walls of which are some strange-looking photographs of the proprietors in carnival costume, their mitre-shaped hats like something out of a Hieronymus Bosch painting. I wonder what happens in these sedate, respectable rooms when the doors are locked and the mitres and strange embroidered gowns are worn? What archaic ceremonies happen? Are there sacrifices? Or do these Dutch villagers just like dressing up? Pictures aside, the Van Der Geest is a decent watering hole for those who want a less frenzied time than that offered by De Schotse Bar directly opposite.

It's a Saturday lunchtime, which means Café Van Der Geest is a mix of Brits and Irish and a younger set of locals who come to listen in to this often rowdy, expressive crowd, and sometimes look to bait them. Always a lively mix, meaning you have to be on your toes. Certain seats at the bar are guarded as if by a historical right. A Scottish lad berates me for sitting in his seat. He points to a plaque with his name on, to prove it's his seat. That is some achievement, when you think about it. Then without warning I get my ear chewed by a tough Irishman I've not met but have heard about, who has seemingly taken an instant dislike to me. I am a colonizer and an arrogant wanker to boot. His partner, who turns out to be English, gently pulls him away. These two encounters rattle me; though maybe they're not just or even anything to do with me being English, but more that I'm palpably not yet an accepted part of the class of people who have given everything to stake their claims here. I am still relatively fresh, from 'home'. To take the heat down a notch I chat to the Welsh Poet, who has just popped in to get refreshed, purely as a way to fully sober up, while Black Sabbath gets their shopping in. His huge touring bike is parked up outside. He tells me that after I left last night they went to the Sandpit, where a full-blown party was still underway at dawn.

The noise levels rise with the collective sound of British and Irish and young Dutch voices. I'll find somewhere quieter. Over in one of the nooks opposite the bar, I spy two older blokes I vaguely remember having talked to in the last few weeks. Those working a season in the bulbs are often in the habit of passing by places, meeting up with friends at factory break times, on each other's campsites or in certain pubs in Haarlem and Leiden. Most who pop in for a catch-up are on the lookout for work or trying to get money for goodness knows what.

I'm learning that friendships have a fleeting quality over here and you should grab the chance to talk to people while you can. I know I've spent a pleasant enough time with these two somewhere in the last month or so, though I can't remember where, exactly.

I walk over to their nook. One is staring at the wall, talking. The oldest, rocking a skinhead and leathers and wearing silver Doc Martens, is continually dozing off. The talkative one, all in black apart from a white-and-black keffiyeh wrapped around his neck, is indulging in spirals of thought that don't need my interjections; in fact I get told to shut it in no uncertain manner. Now and again the dozing lad will wake up, nod consent to no one in particular and then drop off again. I'm not really sure what's going on, though I think I can guess. I cross the road to De Schotse Bar and sit in the space out the back where a super-confident, tattooed and dreadlocked southern English lad I haven't met offers me a seat. He has a pit bull terrier on a lead. He allows the dog to fawn all over me and, yes, as he says, it's a nice enough dog and won't hurt me, but I can't help feeling I'm having the piss taken out of me. After a beer and a running battle to keep the dog out of my shopping I hit the road. The Welsh Poet careers by on his touring bike, Black Sabbath shrieking on the back, waving a shopping bag in greeting.

Sunday may be a good day to pop into Leiden and Haarlem, to catch up with a different crowd.

VERDANTES ANGLORUM

SEKS AND THE CITY

'AH, MAN, that is a Top Punk Tune.'

So says the lad sprawled on a battered leather sofa in a cavernous anti-squat building in Den Haag. What was probably once a large office space is now a complex of rooms where those into alternative living have made their latest stand. Each door has its own notice. It's tidy: the anti-squatter's job is to look after the basic structure and safety of the building. But it is also noisy and public. It feels like a school, albeit one for adults.

Somewhat older than me, sporting a thatch of bleached blonde hair and louche and assured in his battered combat jacket, this lad is engaged in requesting a set of punk tunes on a punk website that plays punk music. Apparently, and in line with the idealistic nature of this internet thing we are all getting used to, everyone has a chance to line up Top Punk Tunes and the site then plays them for free. It seems the site has access to a lot of MP3s of punk tunes: the internet is a new way to call up half-remembered tracks that are probably mouldering away on a compilation tape. That's the thought that makes the act of requesting particularly exciting. Just one more punk tune. But the site can't keep up. And this lad really knows his punk. His requests get rejected as much as they get played. Not that he cares.

The Ruts come on. 'Babylon's Burning'. Which is a Top Punk Tune.

The punk has a younger brother, a colleague at the factory, who is stood next to me, laughing. Both have strong Wearside accents. Both love punk but maybe in different ways. The older is a committed veteran of 1977. The younger is into Iggy Pop, digging his dangerous lifestyle more than anything. Both have been through the mill in various ways, their nomadic, hedonistic lives showing on them like an extra skin or an invisible tattoo, seen only by fellow travellers. I like both very much.

There's a sudden attack of thumping and banging that rattles the ceiling lights. Top Punk Tune tells us of the noise battle he's having with his gabber-loving neighbours upstairs.

'Those cats upstairs, man. I don't mind on a Friday and Saturday when they have their party. They love that gabber music, those cats do. If it gets too loud I just whack up the punk tunes, man. Drown 'em out. Ach, let's go and see what the cats are doing in the city.'

We grab some beers from a beer crate Top Punk Tune has near his door, walk out to a tram stop nearby and jump onto the first tram heading for the centre of the city, standing near the doors to avoid any ticket inspector who may get on.

I look out of the window, trying to keep my balance as the tram grinds and clatters through the streets. I find Den Haag a weird place. It may be the seat of government and a city centre with plenty of charming nooks and crannies, but there is a distinct veneer of shiftiness here. Everyone is watching everyone else. It's a place of great contrasts, closely packed. Streets that look destitute, barren of any hope or happiness, melt into upper-class neighbourhoods full of quaint shops and cafes. The light seems to play tricks as we clank on past squat grey high-rises, lovely old stone-and-brick city mansions and stucco terraces, and rows and rows of old three- or four-storeyed, red-brick houses in a sort of posh terrace style, probably for low- to middle-ranking government workers. I feel the presence of a thin gauze, greenish grey in colour, that settles over everything like a faded Polaroid, or the screen glare from a sleazy late-1960s European film. Silent menace combined with a dank, sticky sweet ennui you can't shake off.

By chance we meet a girl we know near the parliament buildings. She is someone I have seen in pubs with other groups, a waif-like lass in her early twenties whose stick-thin frame looks lost in a baggy sweatshirt, shagged-out trainers with no laces and loon jeans. She communicates in a series of offhand mumbles. We crack open the beers and settle down on a bench overlooking the seat of government. The subject of conversation moves swiftly from punk to an orgy the girl recently found herself a part of.

'The thing about group sex is the amount of hands. There are loads of hands everywhere.'

Wildly I blurt out something about getting some food. I get stared at as if I have said something akin to sacrilege. Nevertheless, and probably because I'm paying, we try some classic Dutch deep-fried snack food, a croquette for me as I'm the only one who eats meat and a big portion of French fries between all of us. No one apart from me seems interested in eating. Token bites are taken, maybe as a way of placating me.

After more nihilistic talk about parties in the city that go on for days and a lot of veiled references to very hard drugs indeed, we go to the girl's house, which is near the Hollands Spoor station. We sit on her doorstep and take in one of Den Haag's residential districts. The place she lives in is part of a row of condemned nineteenth-century workers' and civil servants' houses between Den Haag Centraal and

Hollandse Spoor, now used as anti-squats. These once proud and still-solid brick abodes feel as if they already don't exist: ghosts held together by their own shapes. The feeling of doomed sangfroid is as strong as the smell of weed smoke, a smell so ubiquitous it seems to be coming out of the drains.

'This is great. I love living here. Just looking at these people. No one can stay here. It gets wild at night.'

The inhabitants ghost past us, leaving their grey, indeterminate shapes on the back of the mind, as if characters transported from an early film reel.

Me and Young Sunderland head back towards the centre and end up in a backstreet Irish bar. Despite the distinct feeling we are there on extreme sufferance, we decide to stay put. We carry on drinking, one more pint being the order of the day, the Guinness being a good if temporary substitute for a wider feeling of wholesomeness and wellbeing, until I realize I have missed the last bus back to Noordwijkerhout. The only thing to do is catch a bus to Katwijk and walk to the caravan.

*

The bus pulls up in a ghostly Katwijk, lit by the moon and framed by the murmur of the sea. Taking a deep breath and mentally preparing myself for a ninety-minute trudge, I walk past bleak functional housing projects: the tower blocks half-visible in sodium lighting, the shadows implying a town from the former Eastern Bloc, scrubbed up and miraculously transported to the Dutch dunes.

I plod on along concrete and tarmac cycle paths, the only noise a car or two on the highway northwards. The plan is to keep the highway on my left and follow the signs to Noordwijk and look out for an abandoned bicycle that will get me home in no time, otherwise it's going to be an unrelentingly wearisome plod in the dark. There is no escaping it, this is an incredibly boring walk: a monotonous procession of flat fields hosting squat concrete sheds sectioned off by endless dykes and rivulets or towering rows of hawthorn bushes. Trees stand silently to attention in straight lines, marking the main roads.

The path starts to run adjacent to the highway. Suddenly, in a clearing, there are bright lights.

'*Hee, jonge man.*'

The bloke who has called out to me and is now calmly walking my way is of middle height, wearing what in the sodium gloom looks like an open denim shirt. He seems like an ordinary Dutch bloke. He says something more in a friendly-enough manner, definitely offering me something.

I decide to keep on walking and avoid looking at the row of cars and torchlight coming from inside them. He's not leaving it so it's time to tell him to pack in whatever it is he has in mind. Maybe if I say I'm English he'll leave me alone.

'*Rot op, ik ben engel.*'

After a brief silence the man continues his patter and a couple more men stroll alongside me. They seem a bit out of it but keen to see what is going on.

Speaking Dutch is not my strong suit. I realize I've just told some-one in this clandestine pickup point that I'm an angel (*engel*) rather than English (*Engels*). Balls.

Laughing, the men continue to walk alongside me. I don't feel unduly threatened yet, but there again these lads don't need to do any threatening. It's approaching two o'clock in the morning and suddenly a wave of tiredness with everything, with life in all its complex, infinite glory, hits me full on. For possibly the first time since I've been here I really miss being inside my caravan. I turn up my northern English accent to eleven on the dial and explain that I would like to walk home unmolested, for I am an idiot Englishman who missed his bus and is now wandering the roads in the middle of the night, like we English do: disorganized and hare-brained people who are prone to bouts of feckless and crazy behaviour that fly in the face of the well-ordered, contented Dutch state. And I need a piss, so may I use the side of one of your cars, in keeping with my birthright?

'Hey OK, no worries, take it easy, take care.'

Not bad lads really, just looking for fun outside of their regulated, outwardly content lives.

I don't look back.

About a mile down the road I find an old bike, mucky and rattling but serviceable. Now I am able to increase my speed threefold. I am twenty minutes from my caravan. Once there I open the door and, not caring to lock it, fall into a deep sleep.

END OF SEASON

IT'S HALF PAST SEVEN on a Friday morning in late June. A battered van turns up outside the factory gates. Some of my colleagues commute in from Den Haag and Leiden, using a splitter van owned by a kindly, red-faced English cove who looks like a seaman. He generously does this run for a pittance before going to a different factory up the road. I stroll over and say hi, enjoying the warm sunshine.

The Seaman, bleary-eyed and smiling, is skinning up to the sound of an insistent bass-driven beat. People tumble out of the fug-filled van, an assortment of thin, bent bodies bedecked in dun-patterned scarves, beads and assorted hippyish accoutrements, camo gear and huge DMs, black anarchist threads and leather. There is a noticeable smell of indica, sweat and dust. One English lad, a quiet soul with a shaved head save for a small topknot, doesn't look well. He's a music nut obsessed with drum and bass but this won't help him sort the large weeping boil on his neck. It looks infected. Right at this moment he's on the receiving end of a lecture from a dreadlocked Scottish girl, all attitude, para boots and vim.

'Man, you can use Ayurvedic medicine for many things but your neck needs real drugs.'

The other talk coming out of the van involves 'getting out of it on ket' in Den Haag the night before. There's just time for those onboard to grab a coffee.

It's the last week on the factory floor for many, and there is an air of expectancy, even mutiny, abroad. There is little work to do in any case, and nothing the floor boss can do about it save sending people to restack pallets, water the remaining plants outside and clean out the factory using the large, hand-steered industrial cleaner. The schlep and stress of a season is about to come to a temporary end for many. Regular staff get on with the more demanding things like stock counting and maintaining machines.

Listening in as I pretend to do some work, the talk is almost exclusively about money and travel. People are counting up the weeks they've been working to see if they have the right number of hours to claim unemployment benefit. Friendships and pacts are being formed amongst the packing aisles to ensure that giros get cashed and rents get paid in absentia. Some, like the Christian Girl from Middlesbrough, are telling me they are flush with the money from the holiday stamps they've built up from work in other factories. These are vouchers in lieu of wages, cashed out in May. The Christian Girl quite fancies a month's raving in Goa, if she can get away from her Leiden flat without anyone knowing.

Some colleagues are leaving to begin work in Denmark picking strawberries. Others, like the Scouse Philosopher and the Scots Girl, are off travelling; Thailand, Goa, Vietnam, Greece and Israel are the names I hear floating about me. Those who don't have as much wanderlust are going to have a couple of weeks free before starting in the factories round about. All options offer a supply of hedonism and funds in some form or another. And the upcoming lull in work options will mean a mental fortnight of partying in the many squats in the surrounding area. According to the Ulster Girl and her mate, there are a lot of free festivals to hit, too. I won't be bored.

Incredibly the organization charged with doling out the Social Security to these ravehounds is called the GAK, an acronym for 'Gemeenschappelijk Administratiekantoor'. The joke is definitely on them, not that they would know it. Not having enough weeks under my belt to claim GAK, I'll have to work at least one more season before I can do similar. I feel left out, even from the local scene, as most of the Dutch workers will quietly find employment in another factory, carrying on as if nothing untoward has happened. They may pop down to one of the nearby beaches to unwind on an evening. For me, a late summer of workless, penny-pinching indolence relieved by the odd free festival lies ahead.

It's the last week for the Catalans too. This contingent have been ploughing their own, self-sufficient furrow in a corner of the factory since day one. They live in a squat or commune of sorts in Haarlem with other Catalans, Basques and Spanish in a state of relative autonomy. Dress sense is based around two main staples: mountaineer leggings and huge scarves, often with the Palestinian keffiyeh. The Catalans have been bringing pre-cooked omelettes to work all season. They share them out with all of us at first break, on baguettes cut lengthways, smearing crushed garlic on the bread in place of butter. It's very decent of them to feed us. The Dutch regulars look on askance. Crushed garlic rubbed into bread? Nothing, though, breaks the Catalan mood. Their affability probably stems from their innate sense of solidarity. On this last day the red-haired matriarch of the clan is in great spirits, rousing her troops by singing and popping off to the toilet or outside for a sit-down and a roll-up as many times as she can. Probably just a little trick to wind up the regular workers and the floor boss. Her combat-trouser pockets are as ever full of fags, sweets, pills and ointments. She's brought in some acorn liqueur to share around later. It looks lethal.

After the first break the day begins to drag. I'm outside for a *sjeggie* with my pals the Welsh Poet and the Bray Wanderer, a big, avuncular Irish lad who has settled down in a nearby town with his Dutch partner and their newborn child. Both lads are exercising their unspoken right to have a cigarette on works property while searching for a plant stored in the outside section, which is hidden from enquiring eyes by trees and tall hedges. This is a deliberate and calming process, second nature to nearly all my colleagues. I don't smoke but I too am exercising the unspoken right to have a cigarette on work property, albeit by proxy. Plus that plant could be hard to find.

'I can't see that plant, can you?'

It could take an extra five minutes if we don't combine our nous and expertise.

While we do this I think about the righteous and necessary act of hanging around. For many, sitting down and just relaxing is a momentary high point in a day otherwise spent on their feet. Leaning against something is also an activity to be indulged in, momentarily displacing the clammy, damp warmth stored in the inner soles of your boots. Legitimate sitting down can be carried out on the works toilet, a place that has stockpiled the frustrations of many an international worker in graffitied form over the years. For some mysterious reason, there are often boot marks on the toilet seat, as if someone wants to regularly inspect the primitive aircon pipe.

On this last day, those lucky enough to command the electric car or forklift are gliding up and down the aisles, parading a bastardized form of ennoblement, enthroned on something going somewhere and not prey to trivial questions about what they're doing. Perched atop the industrial cleaner, Serge Gainsbourg has been trundling around the factory floor nonstop: since the start of the day, in fact. No one seems to stop him. Eyes glazed, communing with his thoughts on the astral plane, he indulges in bleating noises and the odd gruff, very French bark. Untouchable and inscrutable, we all feel his offended intelligence.

But *chapeau* to Gainsbourg, he's managed to stay sat down all day so far, and in plain sight too. Nothing beats a proper, illegitimate sit-down, though we have to do it when no one's looking. Sitting down is not to be sneered at. I consider the inalienable truth that only those who have never worked with their hands or stood for hours on a concrete floor sneer at those who choose to take a breather during manual labour, thinking this is a sure sign of the idleness of the labouring hand. More fool they.

The Bray Wanderer lights a standard fag behind some crates. The Welsh Poet deliberately and lovingly rolls his tobacco into the groove of the paper and licks the gummed strip, a further twist of the fingers ironing out any lumps and knots. Fire is applied to both forms of smoke, followed by a quick look round, while large hands shield the fags from the wind and prying eyes.

We chat and stretch limbs.

Luckily we find the plant just as the floor boss comes to find us.

Afternoon. Delirium. There is word from the office of one very big, very late last order from some deranged institution that is looking to plant upwards of a thousand mini conifers somewhere they will not be wanted or needed. The lorry is expected at four o'clock. Me and the Scouse Philosopher are preparing the trees. It's a very simple job and, in the words of Kasper, 'It goes like this.' We cut up white sheets of towelling made of a fibrous, cotton wool-like substance into long strips. We soak the towels in a shallow plastic container filled with water. These towels are wrapped around the roots of the tree, then we stand behind a tall table with a conical metal aperture in the middle. A hefty roll of elasticated cotton-net bandage is placed round the aperture's rim. Pressing a pedal under the machine makes the aperture judder, shaking the netting down and making a sock of sorts to wrap the tree in. We then dunk a tree, its root wrapped in the cotton-wool towel, into this shaking, clanking opening, twist it a few times, pull it out and cut it loose with a sickle.

The noise the process makes is terrific, numbing. It's like standing next to a concrete mixer. By last break at three o'clock, the Scouse Philosopher and I are howling with the noise, barking mad, covered in the dry dust of the conifer roots and itching from their pungent sap. The incessant beat of half-recognized songs on the radio makes everything an awful lot worse. The thousand or so trees are stacked on small pallets on trays with a metal-wire bottom known as *gaasbakken*. These are wheeled over to workmates who start to pack them in long card boxes, the hiss and thwack of the pressure guns resounding around the factory. The music goes up and the boxes are rolled down the conveyor belt where the Welsh Poet and Mr Oz, a genial lad from the south-west of England, are building and shrink-wrapping pallet after pallet.

Late in the day, John Lennon's 'Imagine' comes on the radio. For some unknown reason this triggers Serge Gainsbourg into a fuming and ear-splitting attack on this paean to the glories of peace and friendship. He twists his soft French accent into a parody of itself, asserting his innate showmanship and control of the situation through a charade of nasal honks and rolled 'r's. These, alongside howls, strangulated approximations of animal noises and foghorn blasts of pure Gallic rage, accompany Lennon's gentle message.

'Non! I canNOT eeemajeeen!'

'A brozerhood of sheeet!'

The lorry is loaded up. A fitting end to a season's hard toil. I suddenly realize with a sense of great relief that I don't have to listen to Carlos Santana and the Product G&B's 'Maria Maria' for some time.

A party on the lawn in front of the factory: the bosses' treat for us doing our bit. Most of the Dutch office staff join us warily, some clearly unsure how to proceed outside the confines of the working day. Others look to josh with us, telling weirdly inconsequential, jokey stories about how they find Britain dirty with its litter and cannot understand why Spain and Britain have such shocking, visible poverty. While doing this they stand legs apart and hands in pockets to show they are just as cool as anyone else. When they finish they turn around and form an inwards-facing circle to talk loudly amongst themselves. This is their way of showing that they are having fun. We grunt some form of assent and crash down on the recently mowed grass, staring blankly around the squat factory complex. A small company of modern-day Goths and Vandals having a fag break after the sack of Rome, indulging in endless roll-ups, taking cautious sips of the Matriarch's lethal acorn liqueur and luxuriating in the midsummer sun. Now and again the incessant whistling peep of an oystercatcher cuts through overhead. They really are noisy, fretful birds.

We are treated to crates of Heineken, stored in the koelkast, and an array of borrelhapjes, brought in from a local snackbar. Borrelhapjes are fried snacks that contain a roux made from animal bones and offcuts, flour, salt and some binding agents. They come in different shapes to denote their content. Most shapes are strictly for the meat eaters; vegetarians have to content themselves with the variety full of melted cheese, which may as well not be cheese. Dutch youth seems to live off snackbar food to the exclusion of all other foodstuffs. I eat the borrelhapjes. It's warm food made by someone else: a delicacy.

The Heineken makes tongues wag. There is a discussion that starts to get serious about a book written by ex-goalkeeper and New Age prophet David Icke.

'No, man, *And the Truth Shall Set You Free* is a good book, he's fundamentally right in what he says.'

'Getaway man, there's all that rubbish about lizards in it. We're not being run by lizards.'

'There are a lot of things we don't immediately see in this world. Icke gets that.'

The regular factory hands stand on the rim of these debates, smiling and chatting quietly amongst themselves. They have no need for the lizard conspiracy: they have a perfectly ordered life and seem to revel in this stolidity in front of us, with our cares and fantasies about the world. I hear Kasper talking to no one in particular about his fishing exploits, specifically how he knows where a particular carp is, and that he's got its number. Jasper, a quiet, weather-beaten man in his fifties who looks after the plants, is half-listening. I sidle over. Jasper looks at me glumly over the top of his tinted bifocals, nursing an empty beer bottle that he seems loath to swap for a full one. I ask about his plans for the weekend. I'm planning on going into Leiden to look around some more. It's a beautiful city, with plenty to do there.

'Leiden? I live in Sassenheim. I don't need to go to Leiden. If I want to eat out there is a Chinese takeaway and plenty of cafes. I don't *need* to go to Leiden for that. Hah!'

Jasper tells me in so many words that he has a palpable disdain for Leiden and a number of other Dutch cities. He previously told me he was in the Korps Mariniers, the Dutch Marines, and was posted all over the world. That was before he happily settled down to tend the plants in the factory and the factory greenhouse, situated on a quiet plot of land a few kilometres up the road. There's little I can say back.

Soon afterwards the bosses and office staff, having run out of bad jokes about the problems of Britain and Ireland and Spain, grin impatiently at us. They are evidently ill at ease with the potential for a number of unkempt and increasingly voluble travellers to camp out on the greensward in front of their office. They make signs that it's time to pack up. A blot on the landscape, that's what we are.

A ragged group of us go into Lisse and hit a coffee shop where weed can be bought and drinks drunk. This joint has the feel of a seedy youth club. The grinning lumps who make up most of the customers at the long dark bar don't do much for the place either. Like smalltown bars the world over, it reveals its boring side after a while despite the huge, totemistic Native American sculptures and obviously planned graffiti decorating the place. The talk is of getting the bus to Leiden. I tag along and we hit a popular 'international bar' with a huge terrace that, given the clientele, may as well situated in a backstreet in Blackpool than this chirpy Dutch city.

*

I have lost everyone I came with but have met a bunch of people I vaguely know, and fall into a long conversation with two affable and articulate fellows in their forties. One is from West London by way of rural Ireland, the other from a Cumbrian town. Wearing a combination of old band T-shirts and army surplus, both look like they could instantly fix a leaking gutter or plaster a wall for you, if you asked nicely. Having taken root in the country since the late 1980s, they know the ins and outs of the Dutch systems of casual labour. And, like many restless spirits of a certain age I've met here, they were electrified by the first wave of punk in the UK and can't quite shake it off. We talk of punk in 1977 and their part in it, a subject that, in this happy hardcore-tastic 2000, may as well have taken place in the reign of Cheops. After a while the conversations turn to the many iniquities doled out on the poor British labourer by the Dutch state, where various friends are going with their money and who should keep off the drugs. Some Scottish lads join us, obviously in love with Robert Carlyle's Begbie from *Trainspotting*. Talk turns to who deserves a kicking for stepping out of line and the efficacies of cocaine for treating a sore tooth. Maybe I'm stuck-up, cosseted and squeamish but it just sounds like more roleplay.

The three of us shake the Scots lads off and move to a series of bars. Some are seedy, glorified coffee shops, others ridiculously posh *bruin cafés* where professorial types and girls-with-pearls look nervously on as I am regaled with stories of squatting, London lowlife, where to get work over summer, the Dutch work ethic and 'lost' punk bands like Chelsea, the Lurkers, the Ruts and Television Personalities.

Night falls. I've missed the last bus again. After hours of listening to the travails of the honest expat working man in the Netherlands and with little food inside me, I stumble into my safety net for such situations: the *shoarma* bar near Leiden station, where, for the next three hours, I sit by the counter under the strip lighting. The small TV mounted high on the wall shows video after video of Europop. I sit amongst a number of incredibly drunk men relearning how to eat. With its hand-painted Egyptian themes, relentless TV furze and grubby furnishings, the place manages to be magical and sleazy all at once. It's an antechamber to the deep, uneasy sleep that will soon capture all its customers and I never tire of it, however many times I end up here. The grease marks plastered around the toilet-door handle are a particular signifier of the countless human hours lost here, later half-remembered in the queasy afterburn of regret.

It's also moderately entertaining watching these normally straight-laced students and businessmen slumped and broken in a state of abandon, covered in mayonnaise and beer splats, negotiating these small wooden plates containing pitta bread, salad, mayonnaise and meat. Men revealed as normal, humdrum and utterly unremarkable, not the paragons of success they sincerely believe themselves to be. The students look like childish, slightly oafish versions of their fathers, wearing the traditional suit and tie that Leiden University demands from some of its fraternities. The shouting-at-the-window bloke comes in around four o'clock. The saturnine owner makes him a *schotel* and stands back impassively as the fellow lets loose a stream of incoherent abuse at anyone passing by. Particular ire is reserved for any woman passing the shopfront. At this hour it's often groups of squawking girl students going home. Their blank-eyed, Teflon-coated comings and goings seem to create a force field around them. No one can get close to these girls who attend the university as their mothers and grandmothers did before. The other group that gets a gobful from the shouty bloke is the crowd of tramps who frequent the station asking for small change. One of their number is a slight woman, normally dressed in spangly leggings, bomber jacket and baseball cap. She's a regular sight, flitting between commuters, asking them to make up the amount she needs to spend a night in the homeless shelter.

Dulled by hours of upbeat Europop and spiced meat, I wait for the Rembrandt bottle bar to open at five o'clock. It strikes me, while sitting next to the postmen and fishermen who make up the early crowd, that the intense friendships or aversions I built up with my workmates actually mean very little. This is why books don't get given back, rounds aren't reciprocated and bikes are stolen. The freewheeling, sometimes callous way relationships are maintained here is, along with the drugs and tales of wild abandon, a form of emotional armour against the fact that there's no fixed abode to fall back on and a foreign state that doesn't really look out for you, just tolerates you as long as you provide a service to it. Further, I realize that I may never see the people I've spent the past three months with again. It's a fairly sobering thought.

Suddenly I spot a workmate: Young Sunderland. He is running round and round the block in a state of zen, seemingly oblivious to everything. The postmen look up and grumble something about wild youth. I start to count: three laps, then four, he shows no signs of stopping, and doesn't look like he needs company. I drink up and get the first bus back to the campsite.

SUMMER

INTERLUDE: SEASIDE IDYLL

THE CONCRETE IS ROUGH to the touch and hot under the July sun, but then concrete isn't made for comfort, especially if this structure is what I think it is. Namely the roof of a pillbox, part of the Nazi Atlantic Wall that once ran the length of the Dutch coastline. Regardless, it's a great place to sunbathe and take in the dunes and beach. Listening to the crash of the sea, I doze off. Bliss. There is a lot to be said for spending my unemployed summer days in the dunes: a huge nature reserve you can cycle or walk through, and one that leads to the many beaches often full of Dutch locals and German tourists.

I think back on the previous weeks full of looking for a job and working on getting a *verblijfsvergunning* card, a quasi-magical document that gives state sanction to live and work here for years to come. This process involved being witness to a series of mild kick-offs at Leiden police station and a lot of tedious form filling. Looking for work has otherwise been futile as we are between seasons. I could in theory spend days on my knees doing untaxed jobs in the fields: basic, back-breaking stuff often given to the new Polish work teams. But that is no good for chalking up the necessary weeks of taxed work. I shudder at the memory of the last week, cycling around the region's bulb factories, asking for a job. Wasted days visiting nondescript, functional complexes built of corrugated iron and concrete, with huge, darkened glass windows. Looking in from the outside, these windows seemed ominous: caked in a film of sand, bulb chemicals and the collective mnemonic miseries of the workforces trapped inside. The only light relief was in laughing at the obscene sculptures outside the offices, often made from rusting iron and depicting a bulb, a fat farmer or a vague abstraction of a garden implement. Thank the Lord I found somewhere willing to take me on for the first week in September.

But sod work. I look out over the expanse of sand in front of me. The Dutch seem to use their beaches as extended living rooms, utterly at home with lying in the sun for hours, revelling in a collective, unspoken feeling that their birthright is to maunder about a beach on a sunny weekend. Hundreds of people settle down on areas of white sand, marking out territory with towels, windbreakers and deckchairs, contentedly nibbling at a snack or lying insensate: a huge colony of partially clothed but essentially seabound mammals. These feelings of satisfaction and togetherness are those of a tribe whose laws are not for outsiders to decipher.

There is a chance that I could become an auxiliary member of this tribe as I'm now going out with a Dutch girl I met at the factory: an unexpected turn of events that started with a tryst after a clog-painting night held in the Café Van Der Geest, a sort of 'learn Dutch culture' evening I unwittingly stumbled into. The deal was sealed by her painted clogs bearing an incredible resemblance to the cover of the 13th Floor Elevators' debut album. Not the most romantic of notions, admittedly, but a strong enough reason for me. Our dates thus far have been to museums and galleries.

I turn my attention back to the beach. Long rows of beach huts line the top of the sandbar, serving the masses with a basic array of drinks and snacks. These huts are often adorned with shells, ropes and fish ornaments which battle for your attention with huge painted wooden sculptures of First Nation warriors. After a recent attempt to pass time in one I have vowed to give them a miss unless a visit is absolutely necessary. Slipping into the world of a beach hut on a sunny summer afternoon is a confusing and frustrating experience. For one thing it's like being in some sun-bleached dystopian documentary about a lost tribe of bronzed teens with terrifying white teeth. Secondly, no one seems to have any interest in taking your order. Staff interests lie in flirting with each other and turning the radio up when a happy-hardcore song announces itself with its battery of squeals and thuds. You can sit for hours in a beach hut without being approached, a wooden statue of a chieftain your only company.

I note that there are plenty of German tourists about, often dressed in white, slightly separated from the Dutch in an easy enough understanding on who goes where on the expansive sands. Agog at being at the seaside, many gorge themselves on the fried fish available from small portable fryers on the promenade. The sight of the Germans reminds me I've brought a paper with me, and I read of aggro with the England fans in Belgium who find no irony in mixing Nazi salutes with renditions of 'Rule Britannia' and the 'if it wasn't for us English you'd be Krauts' song. Euro 2000, hosted by the Netherlands and Belgium, is reaching its apogee. Places are covered in orange flags and other football-related tat. I'm avoiding it.

Slowly I rouse myself. Where should I go for something to eat and drink? Like the beach huts, the coastal village pubs aren't my first port of call either: they often shoot a line in garish jolliness that doesn't reflect their true character. Many of the sea-facing party tents are full of local youths not best pleased about sharing their fun with *buitenlanders*. Best avoided. I suppose I shall choose one of the seedy bars that emits an air of ennui and barely expressed violence normally glowering in one of the surprisingly ugly backstreets.

My r'n'r is interrupted courtesy of a basketball, which bounces over and lands on the pillbox roof near me. Three naked men, two older fellows and an Apollo-like lad, walk slowly up the slope towards me. The younger one is holding a Doberman Pinscher on a leash. I get stared at and receive a salvo of haughty *goedemiddags*. Yes, you can have your ball back. The dog is allowed to come closer to me than is comfortable. The men look impassively on, naked save for watches and gold wrist chains, obviously unconcerned about the whereabouts of the ball. Maybe they are parading themselves in front of me in a show of dead-eyed camp. I then realize I may be seen as a peeping Tom, using the roof to spy on the gay nudist beach directly adjacent, something I hadn't reckoned with in my innocent wanderings. I mutter some pleasantry and decide to move on and find the least unappetizing boozer I can.

TRIBAL GATHERINGS

IT'S EARLY but the caravan is heating up. The ants, determined and in file, are making their daily trek along the fuzz of my French bed. To them it must be akin to some fantastic adventure across the Patagonian Steppe. None the wiser about the ant mind and not caring to boot, I lace up my desert boots, jump on my tiny bike and scoot off to a neighbouring campsite. I'm off to visit the Welsh Poet. Over a few beers in De Schotse Bar the previous evening, he'd proposed going to somewhere called Crooky's, a well-established and self-sufficient colony of punks and travelling types just outside of Hillegom. It sounds great: a day out.

The campsite where the Welsh Poet and Black Sabbath have pitched tent is modestly situated on a side road bordering woodland. The reception is a renovated bulb shed next to a traditional Dutch farmhouse. Some homily about being meek in the presence of the Lord is displayed on a wooden beam over the door. I wonder if the hedonists who live here see it as a sort of permanent rebuke, or if they bother reading the Dutch at all. I slip round the barrier and see a motorbike parked up at an angle. Not a good sign. Groans and strangled apologies come from inside the tent. It seems the pair of them carried on making a party of it after I left. They're not coming. I cycle back and consider my options, none of which involve staying put. OK, let's get the bus to Haarlem and see what's what. This pleasant, somewhat sleepy city has a number of great bars. Someone from my old factory will be there, or someone who knows someone. Plus I can always get a train into Amsterdam if I get bored.

*

City centre, Haarlem. I'm in a narrow, high-ceilinged goth pub of sorts, a stone's throw from the city's main market square. It boasts a beautiful mirrored wall and a long, old nineteenth-century bar. The place is full of lean characters in black with piercings and mascara. There is a fair smattering of Brits, too. I recognize my old factory pal the Affray, the red-haired girl from Birmingham who sounded me out on my first day at the factory. An original Second Summer of Love raver and the girlfriend of Young Sunderland, she's normally found in Leiden but is also out for a day trip. Affable and chatty, the Affray is always great company. I'm now getting the lowdown on the Crooky's squat complex, which is actually spelled Cruiqius.

'Crooky's? It's OK, I've stayed over there now and again. It's mostly buses and caravans; some are beautiful inside, you want to see them, all done up by hand. There's no electricity or running water, though. You have to get your water from a pump, and if you want to go you sort your own shit out. You dig a hole with a spade. It's smart to bring your own toilet paper, too. It's pretty right on, but they're just punks, obsessed with punk. Oh yeah, they all drink Hertog Jan, you know, because it's an ethical beer!

'But it gets me that they all want to save the world and yet there are loads of bloody bottle tops everywhere, all over the ground. They're all saving up to buy houses in France, all these derelict places, so they can do them up.'

It sounds like Cruiqius will have to wait for a day when I have bog roll to hand.

I'm also getting updates on a new crowd that I'm becoming aware of, based mainly around an Irish couple from County Louth: the Hedonists. They rent a house in Leiden which by all accounts is party central.

'You have to hear something. Lady Hedonist went to this squat party here in Haarlem full of posh hampers-and-champers types and squatters on amphetamine! How weird is that? The Lady had a pee in a barrel that was meant to serve as the bogs and, as it was brimful of piss, was told to push it over the roof! She refused, of course!'

And so it goes on: more tales of low-grade madness, including one about the ongoing psychological warfare the Affray is conducting on some stuffy neighbours at her campsite in Warmond. The original dispute seems to revolve around cooking with garlic, a practice which the neighbours have never previously encountered and violently disapprove of.

The summer light pours through the windows into this dark bar, adding the feeling that we are in a huge sepia photograph from the 1940s. A few other bulb workers join us and it becomes a golden afternoon full of inconsequential talk and laughter. Soundtracking our animated chatter is music that is very listenable: Radiohead, the Cure, the Pogues, PJ Harvey; that kind of thing. No Robbie Williams. It's a rare treat. As is her want, the Affray demands the music gets turned up. The group I'm with starts to get rowdy and there are a few attempts to climb on the tables. Not that this seems to matter: the Dutch goth and biker types look on, uncaring. It's as if there is an unspoken pact that the *buitenlanders* provide the entertainment and the Dutch join in by proxy. As long as nothing gets broken and no one gets ripped off, these tribes get on just fine.

*

A week or so later I bump into some of the Crooky's crowd in a long, large bar called Murphy's Law in Hillegom. Murphy's is a legendary place. The stories go that one can enter on a Thursday evening and come out smiling on a Tuesday morning. It's also a meeting point for the large contingent of settled long-term workers, sympathetic locals, punks and travellers. The reason I'm here is that my girlfriend knows some of this crowd and wants to catch up with them. When we walk in the Crooky's people are in a group, eating and drinking what may be a weekend-long fill-up-and-catch-up session. They look like handy outdoors types, sure of themselves. I start talking to one lad who welds things, likes punk and has a touring bike and daft dog. Others come over to say hello, all of them confident people, no strangers to a party and pretty canny on the uptake. Yes, there is the punk chat the Affray warned me about, but that is something I am happy enough to indulge in. More interesting to me, there is a great deal of talk around skills such as carpentry, welding, fixing engines, plumbing and learning languages. This lot can certainly take care of themselves.

'You should come over man, I'm welding a fence. Do you like Iggy?'

LAY OF THE LAND

BUMMER. My girlfriend has found a job in a factory with the Ulster Girl from the campsite. There is nothing to do outside of improving myself so I learn more Dutch, sitting in the caravan, alone. Repeating Dutch phrases to myself, I also glide around the wider area for hours on my bike, the landscape sedated and dun-coloured or flattish green after its brief, radiant show of colour during late spring. This view makes you tired just looking at it. I move on. The unremittingly dull-grey glare of the cycle path starts to imprint itself on my mind's eye. Red-and-white-painted metal poles planted firmly in a path to mark an upcoming junction and the path-side benches and trestle tables that are often found in the weirdest, most out-of-the-way locations (sometimes facing a huge hedge or a cluster of greenhouses) become totemistic elements that add to the dreamlike nature of these solitary days. They are the only regular company I have. The minor tremors from the uneven, well-worn concrete paths occasionally break me out of my reverie.

Slowly I draw up a psychic mind map of the area. I start with the bulb villages and towns. Hillegom, Vogelenzang, Noordwijk, Katwijk, Zandvoort, Bloemendaal, Sassenheim, Lisse, Voorhout, Lisserbroek,

Abbenes, Kaag, Warmond, Rijnsburg, Oegstgeest. All secretive, functional, unperturbed, neat and inaccessible. Entrenched bastions of the Dutch provincial mindset. *Doe maar gewoon!*

Noting hippy and raver settlements becomes a casual hobby. For a country with a well-publicized housing shortage, there seem to be a lot of empty properties that look lived in. There's that graffitied house across from the Engel bus stop between Sassenheim and Lisse. Curtains drawn, never a sign of life. Or the glorious nineteenth-century mansion just behind the railway bridge in the posh village of Warmond that looks like the setting for a psychedelic vampire film from the 1970s. Then there's a dilapidated bulb shed of sorts that stands in direct view of the white church in Noordwijkerhout. I think my old factory colleague Serge Gainsbourg lives there, in a reverie.

Various old shacks in fields also look occupied. These are weather-beaten and graffiti-strewn, but serviceable for foreign hermits. I note more cavalier structures. Who owns the large teepee complex on the road running out of Noordwijkerhout towards Noordwijk? Heads of some sort, surely. Or the cluster of souped-up travelling vans with drawn curtains on the Haarlemmertrekvaart between Lisse and Hillegom? This is the major tow canal running through the entirety of the Bollenstreek. It seems to be a hotbed of deviance, what with all the houseboats, decommissioned army wagons and sheds. One night over a beer in De Schotse Bar I am told by my girlfriend that these dwellings have seen wild parties, dodgy people, vendettas. I know one soul who lives near here, a decent and intelligent lad whose twin passions are motor racing and a pet python that likes to escape from time to time.

I check out more respectable dwellings in the area, trying to suppress feelings of envy and longing. Hilary's, also known as De Bols Bar, a no-nonsense restaurant next to the railway track on the road between Noordwijkerhout and Voorhout, is one such. There's a raised annex at the back where An Garda Síochána lives in a state of splendid isolation with his Heineken and TV. Then there is the Hotel Sollasi complex, a long-stay chalet park for workers which overlooks a large lake. I drop in on those staying at the Van Der Geest as well as other hotels in and around Hillegom and Lisse. Imagine: a real roof over your head. To the caravan dweller living on a contract that expires in the autumn, these arrangements seem palatial, akin to winning a golden ticket to the Chocolate Factory. Even so, friends who live here tell me of being stared at through the windows by neighbours. Landlords come round unannounced, to check that these foreign types aren't up to anything improper or illegal.

Other trips take up more time and effort. Before I left the factory I photocopied some pages out of an alternative guide to Amsterdam and the two provinces of Holland. The information is written in an urgent manner, the sort of post-rave, millennial prose that promises some form of enlightenment. I learn where to find the best alternative hangouts and cheap food, when the best free festivals are and what right-on organizations I should look out for. Using these notes and the leaflets and maps from each city's tourist office, I start to get a handle on the Dutch cities: their character and what their inner voices whisper to me. I use a notebook to capture my impressions.

LEIDEN

A student city par excellence, scruffy but charming and high-spirited. Full of higgledy-piggledy streets, worn houses and tough but mostly friendly pubs. Wonderful, old-style stuffy museums and a train station that never sleeps. The glorious Sam Sam bar, where the owner sits like a miniature Buddha in a fog of weed smoke. A hotbed of small-time 'landlords' and subletters, well versed in trading contracts for dingy flats at exorbitant rents. Friends live in rooms above shops, divided by a curtain to allow an extra bed; these spaces are olfactory traps for the smells of the fryer or kebab rotator below.

DEN HAAG

Forever murky, even in the sunlight; the feeling you are being watched is ever present. A silent and uneasy alliance between a no-nonsense working population and a *soi-disant* seat of power. Pubs are secretive and worn-down wooden dives, watchful Irish and British bars or ones that serve up an almost comedic camp-posh scene replete with plastic flowers, a clientele wearing flaming pink or pinstripe trousers, piped Dutch *schlager* derivatives and gleaming brass. These joints feel unreal and are clammy to the touch.

DELFT

Quiet, almost like a village in some aspects, a place that never seems to have completely divorced itself from the bucolic surrounding countryside. Close, inwards-looking, the churches, the famous ceramics museum and the grave of the Oranges make the centre feel like an open-air mausoleum. The locals are mild enough and keep away from you. The high metal railway bridge gives off a sinister vibe, as does the weird 'snake world' attraction near the bike-infested station. The pubs: old, creaking, but charming.

HAARLEM

Well appointed and prosperous, with enough arty seediness to give the place an edge. Free museum stuff in the market square, backstreet discos. A city-centre red-light district in miniature that hides in plain sight. Alternative goth pubs, posh places to smoke weed, tiny streets with odd book and record shops and hidden museums, actually decent curry houses, huge Irish bars and hippy-Catalan strongholds such as One Love. Balkan restaurants. The strangely desolate bus station. A contented and groovy backwater.

UTRECHT

A beautiful centre, surprisingly little to do but look out over the Oudegracht central canal from beautiful old pub windows. Interesting and scuzzy art and record shops. Elsewhere, the feeling of a posh farmer city closed to the public. A decent and feisty Irish bar near a huge windmill at the end of the Oudegracht. Negotiating the confusing, rundown shopping-centre complex that leads to the station. Tedious train ride back to Leiden.

AMSTERDAM

The canals, each giving off its own peculiar atmosphere, whether grimy, touristy or a well-scrubbed haughtiness. Markets, the 'cat boat', strange eccentric bars falling apart or in a bubble of their own making, Zwaantje, Rooie Nelis, Svejk bar, snooker bars and those of ill repute, the Keuken van 1870 soup kitchen with great cheap food and a destitute clientele. A royal palace ringed by squatted and pimped streets, splashed in graffiti and piss. That weirdly normal-looking bar where you can inhale a bag of weed smoke if you so wish. Squads of British men walking in patrol formation through the dank red light and the fuzzy interzone of the Leidseplein. The endless neon grotesquerie of the night train, debauchery on green seats.

I TRAVEL

'DUTCH TOILETS ARE ... well, an experience.'

My mother is telling me about her and my father's experiences of staying in a chalet on Kaag island. They weren't expecting such a spartan welcome. My folks are here for a week, anxious to see the country I've pitched camp in. My mother can't get over the wide and varied range of public toilets on offer. My dad says the country often reminds him of the early 1960s. I nod, anxious to be agreeable while they are here. Other subjects, such as what I think I am doing with my life, are left on hold. Playing happy families, we undertake a series of day trips in my father's car. For a small country, the Netherlands has a remarkably diverse landscape. The flat and well-ordered fields of the Bollenstreek, which stretches through Noord and Zuid Holland, slowly transforms into bucolic arable pastures the further inland you go. We drive through the endless seafronts, grassy islands and waterways of Zeeland and the gorse scrub and deciduous woodlands of the Hoge Veluwe. We are dazzled by the glazed tile roofs of Friesland with the province's distinctive, omnipresent flag showing a red water-lily leaf running between the blue and white stripes. Winding roads in Drenthe come as a shock after the straight highways of the west; we take time to inspect the *hunebedden*, ancient stone sentinels on the roadside, confirming the province's inherent silence. The immersive experience of crossing the IJsselmeer dam and looking down from the Breezanddijk from one sea to another are things we won't forget.

Water. Everywhere water. Seas, lakes, canals and ship canals, fords, rivers and rivulets; water demarcating the green fields and the narrow villages on the IJsselmeer coastline, or quietly irrigating the green heartlands around Utrecht and Groningen.

Strange signifiers are to be found all over this quiet, surprising land. Denoting what? Impossible to say. Three examples: the strange, silent metal bird, something like eight feet in height in the shape of a starling, standing next to a row of parking places in a backstreet in a northern town. Edam? Purmerend? Alkmaar? Bert and Ernie snackbars in Delft and other places, the imposing cow statue called 'Mother' in Leeuwarden. What rites are carried out to become part of her tribe?

*

My parents leave and time continues to drag itself through high summer. There is no spare energy outside of sitting down on a bench strategically placed outside a house, or on a cafe's terrace. The Dutch code of taking it easy and supplications to the Lord virtually close the country down each Sunday. Sitting on the campsite at any point is a no-no. The long summer days just make the place bleaker than ever. To break the torpor, my girlfriend and I buy a regular summer ticket offer from the national Dutch rail service, something called a *zomervoordeel*. This gives three days' unlimited travel for a reduced price. We agree to go as far as we can around the country's borders. As it's a small country we try to do it all in a day. I make more notes in my book.

A Sunday morning in August. We have sandwiches, beer, tobacco, the lot. Sorted, what can go wrong? Nothing, that's what. Holland smells hot. People like us are putting money into slot machines for fags and snacks.

We are on a big double-decker train, riding through a small country. Start point is Leiden, the 'Sleutelstad'. Loons and goons wander around Leiden station, maybe leaving Jazzmatazz or Coffee and Dreams, yellow-gilled and fish-eyed from yesterday's E. They fall asleep in the station cafe while uninterested old ladies chat on in those weirdly rusty voices they all share.

Hollands Spoor at Den Haag. You can alight here, if you wish, for the faceless drug-*centrum*. Then compact, secretive Delft and its leaning spire and high metal railway bridge reputed to be a suicide hotspot. Rotterdam, the concrete-heavy station concourse full of lean characters loping around like wolves. No place to stop. It's hot and bright and we hug the window seats avoiding our fellow proto-Action Man passengers. The smell of iron filings that stale fag ash gives out from the ashtrays is our accompanying fugue.

We are transported over more and more water and through half-seen torpid Brabantse greenery. We pass Middleburg, which looks pretty and self-satisfied. Then Vlissingen, the end of the line, where we alight. Outside of the concrete breakers and a lot of building work there is nothing here, apart from a big statue of some old sea lord and a pub near a windmill that looks like a shed. It's Sunday, so it's shut. We slope back to the deserted platform, now baking in the heat. One way out. Waiting to go east. We look into the houses that back onto the rail track. Dutch rooms: clean brown and cream spaces presented like they've been gift-wrapped, like a bouquet of flowers for your mother. The occupants are sat in chairs, motionless, as if cast in aspic by their own stolidity. Doesn't anyone here move?

The day is becoming a blur. We notice the dark film that descends almost imperceptibly over the eyes when we head east. The light's different: blacker, harder. Darker. Different. We hear the country's true national anthem, silence, enveloping us above the clatter of the train. We notice the black-brown drear of the borderlands in contrast to the painted-on green of the western and central *polderland*.

Each province provides its own screen wipe of perfectly managed non-landscapes. We fall under the notion that this country is one where sweeping generalizations are the real currency. We alight in the north. Getting pissed in Groningen in some godforsaken posh bar serving *jenever*, the real Dutch courage. Yet more experiences of red trousers on rich men; from the very first moment we see them the question lingers: why? After that excitement, headaches and tiredness. A sandwich is eaten in Zwolle's station cafe, maybe the most visited spot of that city for many. Does anyone go to Zwolle? We pull into the functional nothingness of Utrecht Centraal. Time to piss like a camel in the train toilets as the engine rattles and shudders on, back to Leiden.

Small country. We've done it in a day. Still fascinating. Some *voordeel*.

MEMORIES OF FREE FESTIVALS

HAARLEM, SUMMER. Me, my girlfriend and a Scottish mate from the campsite are hitting a free day festival on the outskirts of the city centre. It's in a disused warehouse complex that backs onto a canalized offshoot of the Spaarne, a miniature dock of sorts. The complex has not been renovated in any meaningful way, which makes the whole thing feel like a monster open-air squat party. Apparently a famous Dutch band are playing later; that's why the place is full of people I wouldn't normally associate with gigs. These thrill-seeking day trippers have on the sensible mountain gear normally worn on trips to the Austrian Alps, such as lightweight walking trousers zipped at the knee and hiking boots. They are clearly getting kicks from sipping beer cans in the open and walking round this old industrial terrain. They are loud and boisterous, swapping lowing or long blaring sounds to signify their happiness. People clamber onto barges they shouldn't, and piss in places that aren't for pissing.

The throb of noise emanating from the people and the stages creates that strange, displaced web of vibrations that can only be experienced when standing between dispersed sound systems and mic'd-up voices. A fume of sorts seems to hang in the air, the resultant gases and exhumations from cigarettes and joints, flares, frying meats and supermarket beer. The Scots lad tells us about when he and an Irish mate took a heroin substitute in Amsterdam which rendered them speechless for a day or so. Trying to block out another drugs story, I look over this crowd and pick out the real music lovers: standing slightly apart, showing that strained, slightly aesthetic air of those who need to feel their time is justified with what they hear. I spot the goggle-eyed ravehounds, mostly British and Irish, here for whatever vibes they can claim to feel after ingesting their stash. They are sizing up the estate and planning their escape in an imaginary fleet of Mini Coopers.

The line-up is pretty great, and we get sucked into watching a Japanese band called Ex-Girl who want to give the impression they are from another planet. People groove about in that ravey way because the band is from Japan and different, and therefore demanding of a freaky response. Or so the audience thinks.

I could get used to these free festivals. You see the announcements on roadside billboards and posters, covering all sorts of shindigs in fields; from local kids' events to full-on things like this. The posters are ridiculously obvious, sometimes in a bastardized graffiti style with a tagline such as 'Ultimate Fantasy XIII' and maybe an airbrushed wizard and nymph chucked in for good measure. I like the awful ones sponsored by commercial radio stations the best. These show Dutch girls in a state of partial undress standing compliantly next to a muscled young man sporting mirrored sunglasses and looking tough. Oh, to be enticed by something so deliciously simple as this, the country must be Arcady in disguise.

Back to the action here. In a cavernous hall, doubtless once used for winching in freight, a bloke called Bob Log III, who wears a crash helmet, plays high-octane swamp blues while sitting on his amp, which starts to emit smoke after a few numbers. It's not for everyone. Certainly not the day trippers, but they don't care, it's free.

And that's the thing: free circuses and bread, coughed up by the authorities. Something to enjoy before autumn turns up. I remember a recent visit to one of the commercial festivals in a field outside Den Haag. The music, steered by a procession of nondescript DJs with ferociously gelled hair wearing pilot shirts, didn't really matter. It was just there to add a certain tone to the constant milling around and volume to the occasional beer and burger purchase: maybe a subliminal, non-definable noise that signifies the fact that we're officially having fun. The public tried out some half-hearted congas or vague synchronized hand waving, accompanied by a cheerful grin and those weird lowing noises. An innocent tableau meaning everything and nothing.

Then there was that recent Saturday in Rotterdam when my girlfriend and I went to check out a free dance thing. Rotterdam has a distinct vibe: openly tough, mucky, multicultural, uncompromising and lippy. There are a lot of tall concrete buildings. The station, with its imposing crescent, the words 'Centraal Station' spelled out in big standing letters on its roof, screams independence and indifference. Then there's that weird concrete graffiti sculpture adorning the roof of an adjacent building. What's that about? And why, when we visited, were there so many lads milling around the huge concourse and rows of payphones outside? All lean characters, working on some scheme or other, I don't doubt. I know of only one person who lives in Rotterdam: an Irish lad who would come into the factory ablaze after a weekend.

'You always have food, big man. Have you got any soup? I really need soup.'

The event was a bit shit, to be honest, held in a large fenced-off concrete plaza in a central park area. It was full of uninterested locals shuffling about. A sluggish exercise in urban crowd management, backdropped by the ever-present *doof doof*. We left early, a cup of ice shavings with a flavouring squirted over the top from a lad with a pushcart the highlight. No matter, the event was free, and Rotterdam is a fun place. Getting lost in the city centre when taking a shortcut, we ended up near the open-air market. We hit some bars nearby; they were decked out like furniture showrooms and full of bronzed and permed people wearing sports clothes or overalls and yelling at each other. Having a good time.

Here in Haarlem, things are hotting up. Lots of nice people are walking around indiscriminately, not knowing what they are supposed to be doing but excited. It's like a sports day at school. The big Dutch band is on soon. My girlfriend twists her knee climbing off a barge she shouldn't have jumped on. We limp slowly to Haarlem station to get the bus back to the village. It's been cool: a free day out.

*

Amsterdam, early August. The photocopied notes from my alternative guide tells of the annual Gay Pride parade that floats down on the Prinsengracht canal. The text imparts an urgent tone of solidarity with those in the Dutch lesbian and gay communities. It turns out to be the event's fifth anniversary. We decide to spend a day in town, visiting a few old pubs on the border of the red-light district. One tiny place, near a statue commemorating where Chet Baker died, sells boiled eggs and does a roaring trade in *jenever*. It's a tiny posh gossip shop, akin to a Chelsea or Knightsbridge pub in miniature. We soak up the clientele's air of self-satisfaction and certainty. After the caravan, it's like heaven.

At the Prinsengracht things are really getting going. The press of crowds is pretty deep, watching the parade of large, decorated barges chug past. Plenty of Amsterdammers have come out of their houses to show support. Yes, the Prinsengracht is pretty posh, despite its funky and slightly frayed atmosphere, but I cannot conceive of such a thing in other places uniting all the community in an incident-free show of support as it does here, especially in the north of England I have left behind. This is truly another world: maybe the Magic Centre casting its glow.

We watch a number of boats pass, each signalling a certain allegiance within the broader scene. One sports a monstrous gorilla mascot propped up by some very muscular blokes with beards and leathers. It's advertising a city-centre sauna. People cheer, as they do for each float. We pop into a rickety old *bruin café* bar near the water for a pint as the eggs and *jenever* have left us dried out. We are immediately the subject of attention. Lads the world over will turn and check you out when you enter their local watering hole for the first time, regardless of provenance, and here is no different. One older lad is the spit of Bryan Ferry, replete with mascara, dyed hair and a white silk scarf hanging untied around his neck. He's eyeballing me. I'm not sure whether he's telling me to get out or giving me the come-on.

Back outside we claim a canal-side spot near a number of bridges traversing smaller waterways. It's a great spot to watch the boats go by. A number of smaller vessels zip in and out of the main parade with an ease bordering on arrogance. Not for the first time I marvel at the skill of the Dutch on water, whether mucking about in a rowing boat or steering a motorboat or sloop. One craft scoots past, carrying a young lad dressed in a kinky form of seventeenth-century cavalier outfit. He doffs his feathered cap and shows a shapely Lycra leg, then throws condoms towards the crowds along the bankside. Suddenly he is joined from one of the nearby side canals by what can only be an

American family on holiday, dispersed over two pedalos. The meeting is ill-timed. Evidently panicked by the sight of so many boats and their cargo, the two pedalos gamely try to force a way upstream and escape via another tunnel. This proves impossible, the wash of the barges repeatedly dragging the family back into the parade. After a while they give up, turn around and go back the way they came to cheers and catcalls. It's an apt metaphor for this country. You can't beat the Dutch at their own game.

AUTUMN

CRABWISE POWER HOURS

THE LONG DAYS

THE THIRD OF SEPTEMBER, 2000. It's day one of my new job. The radio has just signalled the eight o'clock news. That means I've been working for an hour. The first break is at ten. I'm standing in a dry cell with a mate from my old factory who has also found a job here, a bright and interesting Ulster girl just back from Vietnam. Between stories of misadventures in Hanoi we are counting out thousands of crocus bulbs that stand in towering stacks of *gaasbakken*. First we take down and restack the number of *gaasbakken* we need for my pallet, then we tick the items off an order list. After that I press the lever pedal of my *karretje* with my foot and pull my pallet to another cell or hall, where another kind of bulb can be found. I'll be here until nine o'clock this evening, picking similar orders covering a wide range of bulbs: tulips, narcissi, crocuses, irises, alliums, anemones, ranunculi, freesias and hyacinths. A lot of walking around is in store: it's a big factory.

I'm feeling a bit giddy, waiting for that first coffee. Not because I'm not used to the work, even if I am a bit out of shape after summer. It's more that I'd nearly forgotten that working in a bulb factory is a very sensory experience. The strong whiff of bulbs drying out in trays hit me when entering this morning. This slightly acrid smell is a concoction of many elements, and one that changes imperceptibly when moving between the various halls. It encompasses the remnants of the region's sandy soil, various chemicals used to treat the bulbs, the wood and metal of the *gaasbakken*, sawdust, sweat, machine oil, the concrete and metal of the factory itself, the compressed, 'melted' smell of the plastic nets that the sturdy narcissi are bagged in, the sour 'white wine' smell of sick tulips and the dust accumulated from all of these things. A film made up of microscopic particles of all these elements immediately attaches itself to me. It's something to live with during a season. Apparently we are working on Saturday mornings, so only Sundays will be wholly free of the tangy odour. Some people use various oils such as patchouli, buckthorn or rosewater to cover the smell. Others revel in this dusty film's distinctive properties, seeing it as a second skin.

I remember what the lifting and all these chemicals do to your hands. The first week can be tough as they adjust. I think back to Kasper telling me not to wash my hands too much during work hours back in April as washing dries the skin out, leaving fingers even more vulnerable to attack. The condition to avoid is 'bulb finger', a painful fungal infection picked up from some types of bulbs. I've taped up my fingers to avoid this.

Other sensory phenomena are created by the sound of the automatic ceiling fans in the big halls which dry the bulbs overnight. They create a strangely calming drone, one echoed by the sounds of the smaller fans switching off as you pull open the cell doors, their softening buzz replaced by a weird non-sound, a bit like an open intercom. These sounds have kept me in a pleasant enough reverie for the first half an hour or so, before the day's drudgery really kicks in and the clack and clatter of the counting and bagging machines and the noise made by the lorries in the loading bay start to dictate the ambience. It's the little things that matter in a fourteen-hour day.

This is the summer and early autumn season, possibly the busiest time of the year for the region's factories. And this first day is a blur of learning which bulbs are stored where. The regular Dutch lads are very busy. They seem nice enough but pretty indifferent to small talk. Simply, there is no time to spare, outside of telling me what to do. The day breaks down into getting through two morning shifts, two afternoon shifts and an evening shift. When nine o'clock in the evening comes around, unless you've been sitting at one of the counting machines or driving a forklift, or wise to the ways and means of skiving in out-of-the-way corners of this factory, you will be dead on your feet.

Nine o'clock in the evening. I am dead on my feet. I skip a visit to the pub and cycle straight back to my caravan, whacked out.

On day two I start to get a hang of the bulbs, slowly noting the different varieties through smell, colour, size, shape or, in the case of the hyacinths, the degree to which their flaking skins compel you to break out in a convulsion of itches. I'm also weighing up my new workmates. They are a radically different bunch to the feisty traveller crews of the spring season. For one, the mix is fairly equally distributed between Dutch, Irish and Brits. Among the Dutch there are a lot of old fellas past retirement age. They obviously like the *craic* of work; maybe their neat home lives don't offer up the same thrill as talking about tulips. Wearing dusty old working coats or cardigans, they sit on the counting machines, checking if the delivered bulbs are healthy. I can see it's a profession for fanatics. Then there are the young teenage kids: relations, it seems, of the bosses and regular workers. They are working out their last week before going back to school. For the most part they are a major irritant. Some actively enjoy the work and are eager to learn about the different ways to pack bulbs at the extremely noisy Hachmang packing machine, or how to check bulbs for sickness. These kids are worrisome in the extreme. Why can't they lead normal, carefree lives like others their age?

My compatriots are a mixed bunch again. At first glance they seem much older, many in their thirties and forties, and as many women as there are men. They are a weathered, battle-hardened crowd: individuals who openly profess their game plan to me, even if this game plan sometimes involves taking a lot of drugs. There are also a number who are noticeable oddballs, here to experience the country, or this factory even, by sheer chance. One clearly eccentric fellow tells me he's a dietician from County Cork and that he wants to go to Amsterdam to buy a bong for his mother. His friend, who he professes to share a room with, a small, slight lad from Sussex, seems mildly off his head. He's happy to stand around and stare into space. I wonder what's going on there.

On day three, after two days of picking orders, I am detailed to go to the packing department. A 'big lad like me' is needed to build the order pallets. Things are hotting up.

ACTION STATIONS

'OK, SO WE BUILD the pallets this way, putting the tulip crates at the bottom. I tell you what to pack, you put it on the pallet. Don't forget, first the plastic crates, then the tulip boxes, then the trays of bulbs for the shop, then the loose bags. Then we tie the pallet up with the tape and bring it to the lorry bay. Let's go!'

My new colleague is Giel, an excitable man slightly older than me who thrives on the pressure of getting the orders packed on time. The packing bay is split over two stations. Opposite us stands a dark-haired, saturnine lad called Marcel, who is Giel's polar opposite in terms of temperament. Marcel keeps his mouth shut and head down, and takes his time over everything.

Standing by a tidy lectern-style desk, Giel shouts out what to pack from each order list by bulb name and I move the picked order, an ever-changing mix of crates, boxes, bagged bulbs in trays and sacks and bags from the small factory pallets, onto the large export pallets. The first few hours are like being in a confusing dream, one with frustrations and distortions at every turn. Giel yells out the variety names in a rapid tempo and I'm expected to find the bulbs on the pallets and confirm the pickers have got the right amount of boxes for each order. The thing is, what Giel says and what a bulb's name is don't often seem to match. He's also got a pronounced, nasal, Bollenstreek accent.

'Fifteen hundred Donkey Shot! Seven hundred and fifty Day Ziray! Three thousand Ankle Food Mix! A thousand Cumin! Five hundred Après Coat Booty!'

By the first afternoon I start to get used to the sounds and clock the spellings: Don Quichotte, Desire, Enkel Vroeg Mix, Cummins, Apricot Beauty.

If you want a crash course in Dutch phonetics, pack a bulb order.

Something else about Giel: he likes to emit a doglike bark or growl when things are going well. And when Guns N' Roses come on the radio, Giel will turn it up and howl like a wolf. Without fail. Even if it's the same song he heard an hour before. Which it usually is.

'Giel, you've heard this song three times today already.'

'So?'

I really like him. He is a great guy and we are getting on well, even though he continues to howl like a wolf at Guns N' Roses. Other songs he loves get different responses. An exaggeratedly nasal Dutch pronunciation will greet a track from Doe Maar, a clever Dutch-language new-wave pop band with lots of ska in their sound who were huge in the 1980s. A squeaky yowl heralds the opening bars of a Michael Jackson tune. And a loud 'weeeoow, weeooww' sound will signify some of Brian May's guitar spaghetti on a Queen number, normally 'The Show Must Go On'.

Maybe it's the stress of high season: anything to get you through the day, as packing is intense work. This first week with Giel is becoming a blur of continual activity. Orders for bulbs come in from all around Europe. Most of the orders are huge, sometimes five or six pallets' worth of bulbs, with each pallet reaching up to seven feet high. They are shipped out to garden centres in Switzerland, Sweden, Germany and France, with some smaller consignments to Italy.

The orders trundle steadily into the bay, wheeled in by my workmates. From what I can make out, the order picking is seen as the preserve of a set of English- and Dutchwomen in their late twenties and early thirties, most of whom live in Leiden. All did their serious raving and travelling back in the nineties and have settled down into renting a house with a partner or mate. Either that or they're slumming it in a flat, saving for a yearly winter adventure: one that is more spiritual in nature than getting out of it in Vietnam. They all have plans.

'As soon as we've got enough we're getting a house back home. It's all we do, save up. We're boring nowadays. Anyway, it's not like it was here five years ago.'

'We're off to Guatemala this winter, we've never done Central America. I heard Colombia is really nice too. I think such-and-such is going to Mexico.'

'I'm learning about healing. Maybe doing a course, getting trained.'

'I've got to get her through nursery first, then I'm going to see about a better house.'

'My daughter's coming out from Boro next year, she's old enough. I'll get her a job here, she can learn to do some real work.'

I get these snippets of information while they drop off the stacked pallets of boxes and trays and bags. As the day goes on, some order stacks begin to look liable to totter and scatter their contents around the factory if you so much as touch them. People are tired, hungover or tripped out.

While the orders stream in the music goes up, maybe as a way of drowning out everyone's personal mental chatter and preventing the mutiny that would, according to the regulars, inevitably happen in a quiet factory. The oily fatuousness of the Dutch DJs hangs over the place like a film of car exhaust. Giel struts around the bay like he's cock of the walk. I suppose, in this twenty-by-forty-foot expanse of concrete floor space, he is just that. I am told by Marcel he's ex-military. He certainly acts like he's on the parade square. Giel soon introduces me to one of his special treats: a 'power hour' where, just for the hell of it and to banish the demons invoked by regular-paced work, we go like hell to pack an order. After power hour we clean the packing-bay floor until it gleams. Pallet types are stacked and aligned next to each other to the millimetre. Equipment is given a dust down and straightened. The results are met with a satisfied and jubilant bark.

It's the Friday morning of my first week back in the bulbs and I have reason to be satisfied. My muscle ache is more bearable and I learn that the annoying kids are starting school on Monday, so no more putting up with their insolence for the rest of the season, thank Christ. I'm also getting a handle on this place, able to place people better and work out who the big cheeses are. Who's who on the factory floor is designated by who holds on to the order papers. Having order papers to hand gives someone considerable scope for bossing others about or walking around looking busy. The Dutch lads like to hold on to these papers and look serious, or career around on the forklifts and electric pump trucks with the orders stashed in a folder, while the rest of us sweat and plod through the lifting and stacking and picking work. I don't blame them: it's the way it is.

One thing I've noticed this past week is that if you don't have a *karretje* in this factory you'll have a difficult time. The small hand-levered car is an essential helpmeet if you walk around a factory all day picking orders, or just want to look busy if you're on the skive. Madly, it seems, there aren't enough to go around. The newer ones, whose metal frames are still unbent and have their plastic coating intact around the handle, are highly prized. These sometimes have a worker's name on the sides written in Magic Marker. There are regular fights over who has a *karretje*. Needless to say Giel has two of the best and newest *karretjes*. This pair and a *pompwagen* are deemed essential for wheeling in the orders. They all have Giel's name on them in Magic Marker.

When someone pinches our *karretjes*, even if only for a second, even if it's to help us or in plain sight, and regardless of whether it's a floor boss, a newbie or a big boss, Giel looks into the middle distance, visibly annoyed. The world has, in the *karretje*'s absence, ended.

'Someone's stolen it. Some asshole. Stolen the *karretje*. How do we work now?'

'Why do they do that? Why?'

I find these questions impossible to answer.

It matters not. Giel will walk off to a corner with a few others to have a *peukje*, a quick nip of a roll-up. People turn a blind eye to fag smoking on the periphery of the main hall as long as it lasts no more than three drags or so and the stubs are fully put out and thrown outside the door or into an old pile of soil. When the *karretje* is returned and Giel has had a smoke and a calm down, both *karretjes* are kept within close reach for a day or two, near our desk, until Giel leaves one at the edge of the bay and it is borrowed again.

Without any real status, or any reason to start smoking, I've snatched some downtime during this first week by popping to the toilet. This affords me a two-minute walk and a nice, quiet-enough place to sit down at the end of it. Sitting in the jakes gives my hips, ankles, lower back and knees a five-minute break, courtesy of the legal, necessary and socially acceptable act of defecating or passing water. Vaseline or Sudocrem is liberally applied to inner thighs and crotch to counter the salty sweat build up. Toes are wiggled and ankles stretched to alleviate swollen and cramped feet. Hands are washed with water only to stop them drying out, and fingers retaped to avoid the dreaded bulb finger.

In the toilet I notice that someone has written 'Slayer' on one of the grey cistern pipes. I recognize the spidery style: it's Winston O'Boogie's. He did similar in various nooks and crannies in my old factory. Did he work here? I can't imagine him getting away with skating around on a *karretje* all day every day in this high-pressure environment.

It's Friday afternoon and I'm back on the packing bay. People are winding down, shouting across the counting machines to each other, taking a minute to talk, light-headed at the prospect of finishing at five o'clock and getting their pay packets. Five o'clock may be a normal time for everyone else to finish work, but for us doing seven-till-nine shifts every day, and working Saturday too, it has the dangerous whiff of freedom. I finish packing an order and, slinging the tape under the pallet and walking to its front to fasten the knot and keep the boxes in place, take a moment to look around. The packing bay gives a wide view over the main factory hall. Here I'm able to clock a lot of interesting behaviour. I nod to a stocky man with a flushed complexion in a knee-length blue working coat. He's been friendly enough to me and all the *buitenlanders*. He also spends a lot of time walking around, singing a *chanson* of sorts, something the Dutch call a *levenslied*, with a refrain that normally ends in a burst of 'lalalalalala'. He waves his hands around like a windmill. During one break earlier in the week, some of the girls told me he's invited them to spend Sunday with him at his sauna.

One prize spot should turn up very soon. This is the accountant, who pops in now and then from the main office complex: a shifty-looking cove who continually shuffles papers in his hands like he's preparing a pack of cards for a conjuring trick. His furtive appearances have made my day this first week, though I don't really know why.

Maybe it's because he looks so ill at ease you really can imagine him running off with all the money. And the very thought that he's been entrusted with the company's money is also borderline fantastical to my way of thinking. Someone tells me that he harbours a passion for cars made by the Reliant factory in Tamworth. That can't be true, surely. I just hope he pays me.

Then there's the lad who is always charging past on a forklift. In constant motion, he evidently loves the work and looks permanently wired from his activities. Like most of the Dutch lads here, he's a decent enough guy, though conversation with him is normally about the lorries he's already loaded or his success in finding a valuable lost pallet of alliums delivered to the wrong department. This is his life.

I've also spent this first week learning the names of the regulars. The problem is the ubiquity of certain Dutch Christian names. Everyone seems to be called Peter or Jan or Hans. To distinguish each other, the Dutch lads add a moniker to the end of the name based on a physical mark or habit. One name gets a particularly rich set of sobriquets: 'Nose', 'Fish', 'Moustache', 'Big', 'Hague'. I take my time clocking who is who.

Then there are the Brits and Irish. I pump the *pompwagen* up under the pallet and, giving it a heave, slowly pull the packed order to the lorry bay. This gives me a chance to swap pleasantries with my fellow islanders. Some have already spotted me moving their way and yell out a pleasantry.

'No Class A's! At least not before second break! Don't forget!'

This shout is the mantra of the Biker, a cadaverous-looking lad from the northern Midlands of England. He's working a few feet opposite me on one of the big counting machines. He has a puppyish demeanour that is balanced against a teak-like hardness of spirit born of constant

143

travel and living in temporary accommodation. Charmingly out of control, and someone who will just get up and walk off somewhere else if things don't suit, the Biker enjoys talking about imaginary rock bands, bikes and red wine. He is prone to disappearing into the large area behind the factory where the old crates and *gaasbakken* are stored, ostensibly to 'tidy some pallets up' or 'take the rubbish out'. Later, visibly flushed, he'll rejoin the work. This activity becomes a commonplace. I'm not going to get a lift on his huge touring bike, that's for sure.

His neighbour on the machines gives a nod and throaty guffaw in confirmation. This is the Yorkshire Painter. Red-faced and amiable with years of saturnalian fun behind him, he's a decent sort, long since sunken into the warp and weft of living in Leiden, that city of pub dreamers. He bikes in to work for his health, talks about his partially shelved career as an artist and spends the week dreaming about the weekend.

I'd begun talking with the pair earlier in the week to break up the military routine imposed by Giel. The patter is based round music, history, drink, books, motorbikes, space travel. Anything that isn't bulb-related. We normally watch out for when the Dutch lads aren't paying attention as they grumble if we chat for over thirty seconds, but I am quickly sussing out when good moments come and the other two are old sweats at this game. A casual stroll to take a newly palleted order can last an extra thirty seconds if I tie my shoelace or double-check that all the pallets are correctly aligned. Then I'll be joined by one or the other of these two. The exchange needn't be long. A sentence is enough, a rejoinder to what was said an hour before.

'I've been thinking, what is the speed of darkness?'

Then it's quickly back to Giel and his litany of animal noises and Guns N' Roses.

We start to speculate how long the earth really has to go before it implodes. We invent a whole litany of lost punk bands from 1978, from places like Stourbridge and Byfleet. We name each member and create imaginary scenes, record releases, escapades and sour-faced reviews from the music press. We write new lyrics for Marvin Gaye's 'Sexual Healing' that deal with plumbing and using the correct water-based sealant on leaks. Even with so much to take in this first week, I can see this game has legs. It could last for weeks and take my mind off the feeling of continual weariness from hard work and the realization that both the tempo and monotony won't change much these coming months.

We three take the piss out of those who are making far too much effort, quietly exhorting them to join in our game. Most don't. I start to mark out those who are natural victims of work. The martyrs. Those who think there is a way out of this if they behave. Those who think that being obedient in all aspects will get them somewhere. Those who aren't even sure what they are doing here but are here all the same. One of these, The Yorkshire Builder, is a strange case. He is a small lad with a round, open face that has disappointment etched into it. Apparently he walks to work every day. He tells us he listens to the World Service religiously but has already been early for work this first week, arriving at six o'clock in the morning because he doesn't seem to grasp that the World Service uses Greenwich Mean Time, and that it's down to the listener to know their local times, such as British Summer Time and Central European Summer Time. His work is carried out perfectly and when break comes he sits alone, poring over a well-thumbed travel book. Any mention of life in Britain, however tangential, means conversation with him is over.

Things quickly came to a head with The Yorkshire Builder: on my third day, in fact. Sitting alone at first break, he began a soliloquy to no one in particular about the injustice in Britain towards honest lads who just want to get on. That dinnertime he elected to sit with the older Dutch factory sweats, who were mildly baffled. Some were visibly uneasy about Yorkshire switching tables. Everyone's friendly with each other to a degree, but factory pecking orders extend to the canteen and there are unspoken rules to observe. One of these old sweats quietly asked a couple of us what was going on.

'Hey, why is that guy sitting with us, is there trouble?'

Just this morning a workmate told us that they heard, from somewhere down the grapevine, that he's on the run. We said nothing. Anyway, how would we know?

Then there is the Sussex Trawler, who I noticed on my first day: the chap who stands looking utterly lost by one of the counting machines. It's as if he has been tied to the machine by an invisible leash, straining to get away but never moving until one of the old Dutch guys yells for him to get cracking in wheeling away the full stacks of *gaasbakken*. Now and again he yells out inanities, seemingly wanting to fight people. When spoken to he talks in a whisper and tells about his time working on the trawlers off the Sussex coast and the low-level brutalities of living in a fishing village. He's had a hard time. Cancer has left its mark on him too, hence the moments when his mind visibly wanders off. Right at this moment, from my viewpoint in the lorry bay as I wheel a pallet into the correct order line, he's sat down while the Dutch guys he's working with go off for a natter out the back door. He is soon joined by his constant companion, who is working behind him on another machine. They're inseparable. This is someone else I couldn't help but notice on day one. The Dietician is a pasty-faced son of County Cork, fond of telling tales that seem to have no bearing on any form of reality I know of. He has informed all and sundry that he's studying at university but is taking some time out in the Netherlands on a fact-finding mission to see how liberal it is, which, I have found out, as he is fond of repeating it, involves buying a bong for his mother. His diet seems to be peanuts and Cup-a-Soups.

'You just need a lot of protein, then you'll be fine.'

The Dietician loves Cup-a-Soups, which are available in packet form from a dispenser in the canteen. A Cup-a-Soup is a luxury. Having a mugful gives you the feeling of getting an extra freebie from work. Soup with your sandwiches: there's posh. Popular flavours are the thicker varieties, the glutinous ones that stick to your bones: Dutch pea soup and cream of mushroom. Thinner ones like the new, exotic Thai flavour don't feel like they do the business.

For some reason the Dietician always eats his soup with a plastic coffee stirrer, his nose almost in his cup as he ferries minuscule amounts of liquid to his mouth. Everyone tries to dissuade him from doing this, but he won't have it.

'Of course it's a spoon.'

'It's not, it's a coffee stirrer.'

We never win but we understand the love for these sachets of Cup-a-Soup. They are the one great enlivener of the main dinner break at six o'clock, providing salt and processed sugars to get you to nine. When the end of the day finally comes, the cycle home is often undertaken on autopilot: a tired reverie, a moment to savour after signing off on another long shift. Thank God we're finishing at five tonight.

HYACINTHS AND OTHER HORRORS

THE TIME: A WEEKDAY, any weekday, in mid-September 2000. The place: the annex between the two busy main halls. This quiet, cool part of the factory is an interzone. It seems forever in shadow, where sunlight rarely bothers to make contact with the skylight. A place that people just pass through on the way to offices, toilets or another hall.

There are three large cells to visit here to pick up bulbs for orders. One is presided over by a bespectacled man who plods around the territory with the same sense of ownership a gravedigger has over the outer reaches of the churchyard. We see him in the packing bay sometimes, walking through the factory towards the offices, a quivering mess, unable to stop shaking. His specs hang on to his nose like a shipwrecked survivor grasping a dinghy.

We look on, half-horrified and half-amused. Poor bastard.

This lad, Sander by name, looks after the hyacinth bulbs. This can be a brutal job. Hyacinths are lovely flowers but they are hell on earth in bulb form. They have to be kept at a steady, airy temperature in a fairly cool and dry cell. Given the dryness, the bulbs' skins shed

148

quickly and easily. Light and desiccated husks when detached from the body, they contain tiny calcium oxalate crystals which, if you're not careful when handling them, get onto your own skin and irritate the soft parts of your ears, neck and inner arms.

Worse, September's weather is often changeable, and sometimes cool and cloudy as a presage to autumn. Plus the Zuid Holland landscape is flat and open, and very rarely not windy in some form or another. Ideal conditions for the hyacinth bulbs to do their worst. And today I am the poor bastard who has to pick an order someone's forgotten. Giel's not going to do it: he suddenly has a much more important order to pack. I grab the papers of the missed order and trudge off to the cell. Shit.

It's hard to underestimate what a pain in the arse it is to work with hyacinth bulbs. The day is long and tough enough without having to deal with small, innocuous entities that can bring real discomfort. I pass Sander. He throws me a wry look.

I walk into the cell and take in the pungent whiff of the drying hyacinth bulbs: a close, acrid, sickly smell. Hyacinths discharge a golden liquid that sticks to the metal trays of the *gaasbakken*; it's akin to amber, but poisonous and pungent. It really does reek. But that's really the last thing on my mind. I now have two choices: I can creep around the cell while avoiding touching any part of my body, however much I need or want to, or I can run in, find what's needed and hope to work up a protective layer of sweat in the meantime. For if I've not found what I'm after sharpish, the dreaded itch will doubtless announce itself. Initially it's akin to a mild, burning sensation that affects the face and hands. It feels like a mental rather than a physical trial, probably because you are preparing yourself for it. This unwelcome presence will then make itself known on the neck. Even if it's head-shakingly irritating not to, rubbing or scratching at this point is to be avoided. Washing in a lot of hot water or working up a muck sweat soon afterwards is the best remedy. I'll be putting my head under the hot tap in the kitchen shortly after this, no doubt.

If I was a goody two-shoes I would wear the suits that hang up near the showers. These supposedly protect you from the bulbs' worst ravages and also make you look like an astronaut, but the act of clambering into one and zipping it up, then taking it off and washing it, is a pain. And they also stink of old sweat inside. Many of those detailed to help Sander out don't bother with them unless it's absolutely needed. I imagine those poor lumps from over the years and shudder. Sander's a pleasant enough sort, though he gives the impression that his luck has run out.

I walk out, trying to avoid touching myself, into a blast of 'Piano Man' by Billy Joel. I think, not for the first time, which is worse: hyacinth itch or the radio?

The factory normally plays one of the national, regulated broadcasting stations. It's not as bad as the commercial ones, but the DJs still mark themselves out by the tone of their voices to be self-aggrandizing attention seekers lording over a rarefied circle of hell. Listening to them is akin to being strapped to a dentist's chair, eyes kept open by pincers similar to those in *A Clockwork Orange*, and forced to watch Mister Punch in his guise as Deepthroat, pissing battery acid over the world while riding a pterodactyl. The mid-morning slot includes a regular prank call to some unwitting victim, often a minor celebrity. It's a popular wheeze and I've noticed in the past three weeks that a lot of the Dutch lads stop to listen. Maybe this momentary pause, listening to the wooden, enforced jollity, excruciating punchline and silly 'ironic' jingles, is just there to give everyone an extra couple of minutes' relief outside of break time.

Now and again we get a good number. These normally show up in the afternoon slots when the morning dose of sunbeam happiness is no longer deemed necessary to keep us agog with the prospect of yet another day checking for sick tulip bulbs or putting five thousand crocuses on a pallet. Now and again we get something above the ordinary. The Cure's 'A Forest', for instance. The song's feeling of existential remove, its role as a portal to another place, is a momentary balm to the soul. The hypnotic tick of its beat also helps you chuck twenty-kilo sacks of narcissi on the top of six-foot-high pallets. The noticeable thing is, it's the only Cure track the station plays at all. It's as if a musician's or band's identity, their core message, is deliberately boiled down to one number, for the rest of time. Unless you are Queen, Phil Collins, Paul Young, Golden Earring or the Rolling Stones. These acts get two or three numbers, a ballad, a rocker and a torch song, each signifying a different mood and showing the diversity of their *oeuvre*.

Last Thursday things came to a head between a few of us and the regulars who seem to be immune to hearing 'Californication' four times a day.

'Can we have the radio off?'

'No, that's not allowed.'

'Can we play our music then?'

The Dutch lads relent. They humour us, thinking we can't handle working without 'our sort' of music. We are allowed a morning's trial on Friday.

I decide to keep my nose out of this. At the last Thursday break a pecking order was bashed out on what should be played. I can't be bothered arguing the toss over what music will bring a moment's transcendence in a dusty, smelly bulb factory. Just the thought of a morning's escape from the likes of Shania Twain is akin to a mirage of an oasis in the desert. As there isn't a suitable radio station, some-one will bring in a CD player which will then be routed through the tannoy, and a few others will bring in CDs. I've seen some of these artefacts, all housed in scuffed, tobacco-stained plastic cases that resemble the surface of an ice rink after a beginner's session. They've obviously been used as passenger-seat aides for skinning or chop-ping up 'on the road'. When I get to see what's been brought in on the Friday morning, the choice is as I expected: the stuff that makes the traveller tribes tick. Dance compilations, the Orb, the Stone Roses, Sabbath, Pogues, Massive Attack, Primal Scream. Reggae of all sorts. Even some standard punk like the Pistols. It's going to be an interesting morning.

It's first break time on this busy Friday in high season. We've put in three solid hours of work. Standing in a packing bay where the noise of the lorries, forklifts and bulb machines adds a steady thrum, I haven't experienced as much of the musical epiphany as I would have liked. Some Dutch lads look a bit restless. The one who looks after the narcissi, a hefty, taciturn though very likeable fellow, has developed a markedly red face in just three hours. He has popped into the office.

As we file out of the canteen after break, the *schuurbaas* beckons the English and Irish over. Apparently the music is making some of the regulars unhappy. We are asked to understand that it's not the music styles or anything to do with us. Our work is appreciated. It's just the atmosphere our music creates. It's not right.

'You all like nervous music.'

'What do you mean?'

'It's not easy for people to get used to. Not easy music.'

No one really admits to being the one who had a word in the boss's ear, and no one looks to openly lord it over us. Most of the people working here are all right. They just have their ways and we have ours. We all agree that music is a great divide and tune back to the chrome-plated banalities of what we know. That's why, right at this moment, I have to choose Billy Joel over hyacinth itch.

ICKE PROTECTION

HIPPY HIERARCHIES

PERHAPS THE VAN GIVES IT AWAY. There is something about this particular one compared to the multitude of others that workers and friends drive; something about the quality of its dilapidation doesn't quite feel right. Other vans are battered but capable entities, their tarpaulins, badges, tax discs and additional oilcans proof of their status as veterans of the European roads, from Castille through Burgundy and the Ruhr to Jutland and back to Aberdeen. They feel worked on, part of the conversation, shaped by their drivers. This van is just dilapidated enough to get noticed. Greyish white, a colour that makes you think it wants to report in sick, it bumps its way into the factory forecourt in a series of fits and starts before shuddering to a halt. Its doors open and disgorge four individuals who seem oddly uninterested in where they are, as if they were a party viewing a stately home. We orcs of the factory, sprawled on the grass and otherwise busy relaxing during our lunch break, stare at our new colleagues. Something about them gives a sense of imperturbable safety and almost comic wellbeing. None of us could aspire to such a frayed, fuzzy, raggle-taggle aspect. Maybe it is better while they are here, in front of me, to step back and cast this gang of four in aspic, freeze-frame them, ensure they never escape this fairy tale. The group, now talking in a desultory manner to the *schuurbaas*, are prime specimens of the Verdantes Anglorum tribe.

The Verdantes Anglorum are a loose confederation of peoples that originate from the rural areas of England: from the monied pockets of the Vale of York and the Borders, and farming counties such as Rutland, Herefordshire and Northamptonshire. Their ranks are in the main swelled by those from Home Counties suburbs. Overwhelmingly middle class in origin, with some plucked from much higher up the food chain, the Verdantes Anglorum are normally fair or ruddy of complexion; one could be unkind and say they are apple-cheeked.

Those men who feel themselves born leaders of a particular group, reckoned by how many can fit into a van, make a pass at accentuating their jawline or cheekbones, or cultivating a steady 'mystic' gaze. This gaze is set off by either dreadlocks or a grown-out, often curly mop of hair. They are keen to show you their mastery of dogs, normally Alsatians, Rottweilers and pit bull terriers, to whom they often ascribe feminine virtues. Despite the tough reputation these breeds have, dire warnings as to their ferocity are only given when another dog is in the vicinity. Then curt orders, maybe previously barked out on parade grounds or in a field in Kent during hop picking, ring out. Otherwise, they assure us, their companions are soft, playful and loving.

All the Verdantes Anglorum profess a love of the land and look to cultivate an 'understanding' of the bulbs and plants they throw in boxes each day. To them, even these standardized and treated plants possess sacred properties. The prized job is to work in the greenhouse, feel nature's inner rhythm and smoke herbal cigarettes when no one's looking. It's often an enjoyable exercise to contrast the stolid workaday interest the Dutch farmers have with the plants to the veneration lavished by these sensitive types on, say, a box shrub, as a sign of something bigger and more profound. This attitude sometimes takes on an earnest if faintly ridiculous aspect. Some devotees to the Good Life, when asked, sweetly explain that they walk barefoot 'to feel nature beneath my feet'. Being a 'wanderer' is also an accepted role. Though it must be said that a number of the male elders of this tribe often seek to move in with their partners in their or their parents' homes, looking to form a special relationship with the mother and commandeering the garden as a site of special interest.

Other manifestations of male omnipotence involve a very public concern for their partner's menstrual cycle. This is often a precursor to a wider public display of partnership being something deeper, more spiritual and sacred, and linked to pagan mysteries, yet wilder and more depraved in private than any of us onlookers could imagine. For some reason this appeals more to younger Dutch and German women than their British or Irish peers. To my knowledge no male of this tribe is openly transsexual, homosexual or bisexual.

Some carry their nascent mystic state into literary pursuits, which are often talked about in a quiet, offhand manner. Literature is there to enlighten, and marginal lore is encouraged. However, their reading choices can be surprising when pushed into revealing what they would rather not, and earlier flirtations with the likes of Loaded or Bridget Jones's Diary are revealed. In the main they cite Philip K. Dick, or, if needing to give a more contemporary worldview, David Icke's explorations into the lizard empire. Wider literary and cultural discussions are discouraged with a laugh, as this kind of indulgence would waste valuable thinking time.

Recreational pursuits are normally something to do with smoking Purple Haze or taking 'ket', otherwise known as ketamine. Each to their own, of course, though it often strikes me that trying to be a modern-day Sir Thomas Browne and spending nights on the horse tranquillizer may not be the best balancing act. Some of the tribe affect surprise at the early bedtimes seasoned factory workers stick to in high season, advocating the regular ingestion of speed as a useful way of getting to work on time.

Soundtracks to these meaningful early-hours weekday parties are usually based around reggae of some form, with Bob Marley an ever-smiling presence. Manu Chao's music is also ubiquitous. Anarcho-punk is given a thumbs up in principle. Ozzy Osbourne's Black Sabbath are also given official approval, as are 1990s pop bands like the Spice Girls and All Saints, the latter maybe because of 'Pure Shores' and its association with *The Beach*. Dance music normally leaves them cold, and those Verdantes Anglorum who practise it, quiet men, often shaven-headed wearers of bead necklaces and wide flapping combat trousers, are normally ignored by the rest.

The women of the tribe normally work on an act that falls somewhere between winsome, sleek and jolly. The jolly ones are there to talk to the *schuurbaas* and cook. The winsome and sleek say very little outside of letting slip the odd verbal kicking to no one in particular. Some others, more fun and outgoing and obviously independent of the social mores that bind this tribe, cultivate a feral aspect that can involve openly growing and showing off their navel hair and getting tattoos. Many make huge pans of vegan stew, favouring the vegetables that don't really lend themselves to stews: broccoli, cabbage, cauliflower.

Back to our very own gang of four, standing here, right in front of us. The group comes to some agreement with our *schuurbaas* and join us on the grass. The main talker is nice enough, an energetic lass called Atlanta. The other girl is called Lucia. She contents herself by gliding through the trees like an elf. One of the lads is named what we wonderingly hear as Bonga. The leader doesn't really give his name, outside of a series of gargled emissions that make a wheezy progress through his nasal passage. My chum who works on the packing machines, Total Drugs, a lad from North Lancashire who enjoys taking very strong drugs indeed, christens him the Officer. Bonga and the Officer hold back. The dog (there has to be a dog) is a black Alsatian cross who has the air of a frosty Old Bailey judge (retired). It ignores the foibles of the human world.

Over the week the gang work here, we find out more about them. Bonga encourages us to think he's a professorial type who knows about computers, the Dotcom Bubble and little-known histories. But it seems that he is most comfortable being a rootless malcontent, prone to wandering around the factory and shouting sneering comments about the state of us, especially after we find out from one of the office staff that his real name is Christopher. Atlanta tells us Bonga hates to be called Christopher. Bonga eventually finds himself in the hyacinth department, where he is seen shivering uncontrollably from the itch. People like Bonga, the loners, the ranters, the misfits, the vulnerable, always seem to end up in the hyacinth department.

The Officer never seems to do anything useful. The moniker is a brilliant piece of deduction from Total Drugs, as it seems he must have been in the army at some point. Even the way he leans on his pickup truck betrays his way of 'adopting a casual attitude' with the men.

He comes to work with me in the packing bay. Standing easy, the oaken joints of his skeleton creak into what he would doubtless see as an 'everyman' slouch, much beloved of the working orders. A humourless grin, evidently practised at great cost in front of a mirror, and a 'Rasta Baby' T-shirt complete matters. He asks me how to wrap an order he has packed. Or rather, can I do it for him?

Other sallies happen during lunchtimes on the grass in front of the factory. Lucia, in between plaiting her dreadlocks into what I think is meant to be a Boudicca look, asks us what we do after work. Those who say they watch television are upbraided. Other admonishments follow in a whisper, mainly around our choice of sandwich filling (cooked meats, cheese) and the sedentary nature of our lives. We numbly, resignedly, allow ourselves to be shriven. Shortly afterwards Bonga, backed by the Officer, embarks on a lecture that brooks no intervention on the inalienable fact that the American military are the first to use chemical weapons in warfare. On being told poison gas was being used by all sides during the First World War, Bonga tells us off for having an unhealthy interest in militarism, casting us further into the pit. Atlanta, blissfully unaware of the mounting tension in the wider group, offers everyone a bowl of cauliflower soup that she made the night before. Congealed and clammy-looking from spending the night in the open, this pottage doesn't look particularly inviting. Neither does the pan, which seems to have survived a blast furnace. 'It's lovely when warmed up,' says Atlanta, fighting off definite interest from the dog.

WORKING ON ACID

A MONDAY IN LATE SEPTEMBER. Things are getting really, really busy. People from the office are running round with concerned expressions. A lot of money is at stake in terms of fulfilling some huge Swiss and German garden-centre orders that came in later than expected. The lad who loves bombing around on the forklift now seems to be glued to it. Eyes bulging, he zips between lorries, bringing tulips into the factory to check and store in a cell, or loading packed orders. He's continuously on the go.

Those in charge decide to take on more casual hands for a week. Normally a local employment agency, the *uitzendbureau* dealing with the bulb and plant sector, is contacted. These services dispatch a group of workers, often those seen as permanently unemployable or judged capable of menial work only. Normally a transit van pulls up in the driveway and a harassed-looking girl in a company blazer alights and bustles into the office with a dozen or so charges loping unconcernedly behind her. Each of these lads, it's always lads, holds a small flask of coffee and a packed lunch. These happy few, normally Moroccan, Turkish and Antillean youngsters or Dutch lads who've obviously spent time on the streets, stand around doing as little as

161

possible, and quite rightly, too, until detailed to follow the boss. The girl, who will come to collect them at the end of the day, waves them off, visibly relieved. A day of unrelenting boredom counting flat, unmade cardboard lids or restacking plastic sacks and crates awaits these groups. The jobs are done in pairs, as trusting these hired hands to work unsupervised and alone is seen as a step too far. How these fellows feel, turning up every day to be driven to a different place, doing the same soul-crushing job at a snail's pace, ignored and sometimes openly abused, is not to be countenanced. When I see these groups turn up, I count my blessings.

That's what normally happens. This time the factory needs people prepared to work a week at top pace and autonomously. To be prepared, in other words, to submit to all manner of shit without question, and sometimes even show a semblance of enjoyment. It seems we are in luck: the travellers are starting to come back and are knocking around the factories looking for work. Of course these people are also hit-and-miss, but the point is they normally want the money to cover their summer costs, so will put in the hours. They also, usually, 'know the score'. A platoon of bronzed Catalans turn up driving a big van, the windows of which are decorated with drawn curtains boasting a rainbow design. They are as affable a bunch of people from this region I've met. Portions of bread and garlic and homemade omelettes are passed around and music tastes are swapped. A couple stand out, a striking girl who looks like a hippy and very slim version of Goya's Duchess of Alba. There's also a small, sturdy lad who has a penny whistle with him. He looks like a laugh: a kindly, easy-going sort who can look after himself.

The group are taken on for a week and told to help pick the orders with a couple of the older Dutch lads and the Devon Girl, a good mate who works here along with her partner, a funny and hard-working lad from East Anglia. This English couple are wandering souls, mildly addicted to travelling the globe. The Devon Girl has a dry sense of humour and promises to fill me in on anything amusing.

During the week that follows the Catalan crew seem to bed in well enough. But they have some habits that puzzle the older Dutch lads. Now and again some of their number loll around outside the office, singing. The lad with the penny whistle gives us a tune from the top of a stack of pallets. Some sit cross-legged on the factory floor without a care in the world. They inhabit a different mental space to most of us.

*

It's ten past one on Friday afternoon. The big Swiss and German orders are nearly there. We have a fair number of big pallets to pack before they get loaded onto the lorries at three o'clock, but nothing we can't handle. Everyone is chipping in and doing what is needed.

It's the Catalans' final workday. Earlier this morning, lolling on the grass outside the factory before heading in for the day's work, they invited us to a party at the weekend in Haarlem, a city which all Iberians, whether Portuguese, Spanish or Catalan, seem to gravitate to. We are promised a good time: one in typically Catalan fashion, with lots of food and drink in store. With that in mind we trudged off to our allotted tasks, ready for a day of sore muscles, sweat and adrenalized boredom.

Two o'clock. A number of bosses dash around and between the halls on foot-scooters, looking bewildered. The Devon Girl pops over to the bay while Giel is outside for a fag. She looks flushed, like she's been laughing a lot.

'Bloody hell, wait till you see what's coming. Sod it, just go and have a look in the other hall.'

I grab an order paper, pretending to look for a missing box of bulbs.

Entering the second hall and walking past the packing machine and trays of packed bulbs for shops, I see the lad who plays the penny whistle. He's hunched up in the middle of some stacked trays, crawling around and muttering, looking at the ground. The first thing I think is that he's fallen and somehow concussed himself. I run over to help. 'Shit, man, are you OK?'

He's all right. Red-faced from laughing, his eyes bulge and glisten, and tears stream down his cheeks. Holding a carded packet (the card showing a picture of the tulip variety in the attached bag), he stares at the photo and starts to cry and laugh simultaneously, uncontrollably.

The guy who operates the packing machine, a sour and moody bloke, wanders over and gives him a volley of abuse in Dutch.

'Godverdomme! Stomme eikel! Spaans kankerlui!'

It makes no difference. Penny Whistle turns to me and, with a look of wonder, proffers me the packet. In his heavily accented English his words sound conspiratorial, powerful, as if only me and him truly understand what is going on.

'Theeess! Theeess! Eeeess a booooolb!'

He falls back exhausted as if he's been shot, helpless and adrift on the sea of his imaginings.

Bloody hell, some of the Catalans have dropped acid.

My respect for their tough, raver qualities goes up a few notches. I go back to the main hall in time to witness what could be seen as a Newtonian principle made flesh. The Duchess of Alba is wandering around the hall, making slow progress towards the packing bay. She is singing loudly and incoherently. A cavalcade of growls, words, noises and screeches all share equal billing in her song. She is radiantly happy. The Duchess has done her work and this, her song, is one of triumphant completion. She drags her wobbling pallet behind her, a stack which can best be described as a cardboard ode to Gaudí's cathedral. Boxes and trays of bulbs jut out at impossible angles. No box, it seems, is placed on the pallet the way it should be. Some appear to be frozen in mid-dance, resting on a corner. Others look as if they are auditioning to be a triangle or another, less boring or box-like shape. Small bags of bulbs nestle in the crevices, like alpine plants in a rockery.

Stock-still, Giel is staring open-mouthed at this odd vehicle's stately progress towards the bay. Normally an unstoppable force in human form, Giel is about to meet an order that is, literally, an immovable object, for it is clear that one touch will bring this stack crashing down and spill bulbs far and wide over the factory floor.

'Jesus fucking Christ, what is this? Why? Why do they do this?'

Giel's mind is blown. Shaken to his core he looks at me pleadingly. As if I have the answer. A man in love with straight lines and sharp angles and deeply attuned to the precise rhythms of order, Giel knows he is staring at something beyond his powers: an order that can't be packed, an order that will not be tamed, one that will self-destruct.

The Duchess of Alba has a magical if temporary hold over gravity, it is clear. How else could she have got here, with an order in this state? It is a mind-blowing achievement. She bows, then skips over to the order tray where she picks another paper and then runs happily off into the other hall. No one stops her. A number of lads surround the pallet and start to work out how best to let it fall. Some boxes slowly crumple, bowing to various gravitational pressures, the strain of the positions they have been given finally proving too much. Others simply roll off the pallet and spill their contents onto a tarpaulin sheet that has quickly been pressed into action. The piles of loose tulip bulbs are rounded up and added to the boxes, their sizes, the colours of their skins and obvious differences in shape being the only way to recognize their species. Not every bulb goes in the right box. Someone, some-where in Switzerland, is going to get a surprise in spring.

Giel stands to one side, kicking the ground with his toe. Furious at life and all its injustices, he starts to pack what he can, slamming the crates and fresh boxes down on the delivery pallet. To calm him I join in the packing frenzy and turn the radio up. I remind him the Catalans aren't here next week. After a while Giel emits a short series of satisfied barks as the pallet takes shape. All we need now is Guns N' Roses and he'll be back to normal.

On the weekend some of us go to the Catalans' Haarlem party. It's in a big, rather gloomy squatted building just outside the main ring road that runs through the city centre. The night is a typically easy-going affair, with food, drink and weed playing the main sup-porting roles. Some of us ask: didn't you all get a ballocking? Our old workmates seem unperturbed by the experience. Despite an angry reprimand, they got paid, they tell us, and that's all that matters.

FAREWELL CAMPING

'WHY DON'T YOU MOVE IN? Just for winter.'

It's a generous offer from my girlfriend, whose parents live in the village. I am relieved: I had no real plans anyway.

The campsite officially closes at the end of October, though it's very clear, from the huffing and puffing attitudes that shape his recent conversations with me, that the owner wants everyone out long before then. He knows some people will make a run for it, given the fact the main season is ending and no one wants to pay the backlogs of rent when they could use it for an extra week backpacking somewhere warmer. He makes a show of trusting my inner rectitude.

'You're not like the rest. You are decent, a good man.'

He says this while looking into the middle distance, his way of performing a show of brotherly, Anglo-Dutch understanding. I get a friendly punch on the upper arm. He knows I have always paid up on time. And now he wants my money.

I turn and look over the place. Framed by the blustery late-September skies, the caravan site, now manifesting itself as a series of dank, dark fields housing squat, dirt and mildew-stained vans, is a bleak prospect. The emptiness hits me. Now and again a lone figure darts across the wet grass to get water from the tap or use the phone booth, hunched and with their hood pulled up. No one lounges around the place as they did in summer.

I see virtually no one elsewhere, outside of a chance meeting in a pub. The Polish contingent have packed up and returned to Poland. The Irish girls have sorted out somewhere to rent together, as have the Scots lad and his tripping Ulster mate. The Welsh Poet and Black Sabbath are also trading their tent for bricks and mortar: a converted barn, I hear, with running water and a chemical toilet. Once again my inherent separation from this scene, never really something that mattered in my daily dealings with anyone, is made manifest. My pals all rely on networks forged over years of raving and travelling and sharing wraps of chemicals. Backrooms partitioned by a curtain above a takeaway in a seaside town, a hotel room that isn't officially open and needs renovating, an annex in a squat in the city, a council flat to babysit, stashing the posted benefit cheques while the owner is in Thailand. All these options need time and care to cultivate. I can't be expected to crash in on this scene after six months.

The dunes are wet and dark, increasingly bare and silent, no longer the verdant playground for tourists and tripped-out seasonal workers. And at night the smell of damp, cold earth is much stronger. Not the greatest insulator, a caravan offers very little outside of being dry. Sleeping in my coat is the norm. I shudder at the thought of buying a second-hand heater for this metal fridge on wheels. Mornings are dark and cold with nothing to alleviate the gloom until that first pre-work coffee in the neon-lit canteen.

I accept my girlfriend's offer. 'That really would be great, if you don't mind. I promise I'll sort something for spring.'

After months of no commitments I am committing to something.

A REGISTERED ADDRESS

THE ONTZET OF BOREDOM

THE VERY LAST DAYS of September 2000. It's nearly the end of the season. A new game is in town. The prize is to eke out an extra week or two's work in the factory to gain the number of weeks needed to sign on the dole, before starting another season. Boring, soul-sapping, unwelcome, but necessary. Work starts up again in mid-November. Getting signed on means slowly saving up the money I've earned through these long, footsore, fourteen-hour days, so it's essential I stick this out. I have to look busy, to show I am still of use. I mustn't catch anyone's eye. Keep a paper of any sort in my hand and keep moving around. Do the menial stuff.

Lots of the Dutch lads know this game of old and quietly enjoy watching the rest of us trying to fill time. Some help out and give us things to do, as it means they can get more time chatting around the back of the factory.

The factory backs is an open space bordered by a small canal and a line of melancholy plane trees where all the businesses in the complex dump their broken or unusable clutter. In summer it's a place to escape the heat, noise and dust of the factory, but by autumn it's a desolate spot: a silent and maudlin repository for old pallets and *gaasbakken*, warped plastic crates, parts of machines, old soil and diverse and redundant packing materials. This stuff is normally picked up by a council garbage lorry every few months. These collections of wood and plastic and earth afford a brilliant place for a crafty fag during the day. Some old wine bottles, doubtless brought here and drunk by the Biker in the hot weeks of August and early September, roll around plaintively between the stacks.

Giel likes to hold court here, putting the world to rights with a quick *peukje* in his hand. I stroll out of the back door to persuade him that the orders ready to be loaded onto the lorries don't look neat enough. It's a stain on our professionalism. Plus it surely means a quicker load in. The clouds scud across the sky. The other lads look at me with blank expressions; they couldn't care less what I do. Giel looks at me sideways and nods.

I start a new task: rearranging the orders we have just packed into order of country. Lines of stacked pallets are repositioned according to where they are going. I undertake this job with great seriousness. I move the pallets a foot or so to the left. No, they don't look right, so I do it again, placing the pallets as precisely as I can, looking to align them within a quarter of an inch of each other while taking into consideration such weighty matters as each undulation, depression and minor gradient of the concrete floor, or the minuscule rise caused by the painted yellow lines demarcating the walkway. I reason with myself that if the lad who loads the lorries sees that all the pallets are precisely in line he won't have to keep reversing and adjusting his forklift. It will bring him some peace of mind. This gives me a warm glow. As does the fact that reordering the pallets just one more time will eat up another thirty minutes. Then break time will only be another half-hour away. And if I make sure all the order numbers are at the same height on the side of each pallet, that could kill another ten minutes, too.

This is turning out to be a successful morning.

Giel is all for my initiatives. This seemingly nonsensical overwork appeals to him. Giel has a reputation for being a martinet, of putting unsuspecting casual workers through their paces. But despite his near maniacal obsession with order he's a decent sort. His quirks bring a welcome surreality to a day. It's like being in *Wayne's World*, but instead of two provincial lads hankering after the rock and roll dream of Anglo-American myth, we send bulbs to the rest of Europe and keep the packing bay spotlessly clean. And we have Guns N' Roses, Phil Collins, Golden Earring, Yes, Pat Benatar and Billy Joel to keep us company throughout the day.

I have bought an old racing bike from Giel with some of the cash I saved up. The small bike I acquired in a panic on that first day in April, the child's bike, the bike that has led to over-developed muscles in my core and probably damaged the cartilage in my knees, has finally been sent to the local Kringloop, a nationwide chain of outlets that sell on used and second-hand household items. I went to Giel's house in another village. I said hello to his children and his wife and entered his shed, where the bike was. Everything was neatly lined along the shed walls. Each tool in place, in descending order of size, spaced precisely apart. His work shoes and those of his children were similarly aligned, according to size. It was a joyous confirmation of Giel's character.

*

October begins. There is very little to do, and there are far too many of us. We are gathered here, ready for work on Monday, 2 October

2000, in case a last-minute order comes in. If not, we are all getting our papers at some point during the week. But I could really do with two more weeks, then I will have enough weeks under my belt for the year and can officially sign on for unemployment benefit. Then I will feel that I am at last part of the gang I've been running with these last six months, earning my dole between seasons.

But even though overtime has finished, working these extra two weeks still means eighty working hours spent hiding or standing around looking busy in a cavernous factory. This is as much a mental and emotional battle as a physical one. I consider what to do. If I don't fill my head with something I will end up going mad from listening to the radio. Why not be pious and self-improving and fill my head with Dutch verbs instead? After all, I've just moved in with my girlfriend's parents. It's good to establish a rapport. Yes, that is what I must do, establish a rapport. I don't want to be one of these Brits who shout loudly in English at shop assistants and waiters here. And the quicker I can get by in Dutch the better my prospects.

Monday slowly unfolds. I mumble my execrable Dutch to myself during the morning hours. But I find that repeating verb tenses and trying to find a way not to spit the Dutch out like I've a mouthful of broken teeth isn't easy. Especially while walking round and round the gloomy expanse with a brush, a *karretje* and a few bits of paper, avoiding bosses and now and again indulging in a desultory cleaning of a woebegone, dust-strewn corner of the factory. The Dickensian misery of repetitively doing no work that has to look like work, backed by the dayglo radio aggressions from the likes of Pink, whose strident songs compete with the ceiling fans keeping the last of the tulips dry, is considerable.

Come on, ten more days, you can do it.

One of the Dutch guys soon picks up on my ad hoc language course. He has the sobriquet Nose due to his prominent nose. He's a nice fellow, a bit eccentric and, if we're being honest, a bit of a misfit. Inexplicably he's quite high up in the factory pecking order here, which means being nice to him is wise. He promises to walk around with me while I practise my Dutch on him. We'll speak Dutch together, starting now, this Monday. That's decent.

The thing is, I haven't a clue what Nose is saying. I dutifully repeat the words he says but he has a very strong accent. Not a Bollenstreek one, the wheedling and lowing of which I can sort of get a grasp on. Nose is from Katwijk, about three miles down the road, which may as well be a different country given the way the natives talk. I try not to laugh because his speech sometimes makes him sound like a parrot. Nose tells me that 'Katwijkers speak English Dutch', which should mean I'll catch on quicker, surely. This offer is very decent of him, but the only thing I learn is that the word *ding* (thing) can be used for almost anything, as Nose uses it for nearly everything. And Katwijk, a word he comes back to regularly, is pronounced 'Katweek'. Which makes it English, apparently.

At the last break the Affray turns up on a visit. Her cheerful Birmingham patter fizzes through the canteen.

'Come into Leiden, you have to see the Third of October. It starts tonight. You can crash at mine. My brother's back in town. Tell your missus.'

Normally a Monday night is a quiet night. I think, what the heck, I'm going. Something new.

*

Leiden, seven o'clock in the evening, Monday, 2 October 2000. Scrubbed and a bit stiff from our respective days' work, my girlfriend and I are trying to figure out how to get to the place we agreed to meet the Affray, outside a bar just down from the station called the Goes Bar. That's the English name for it anyway, as De Gulzige Geus, replete with the gargled 'g' sound, is a linguistic step too far for many of us. It's a friendly biker bar in which the casual workers, Dutch bikers, potheads and travellers have made common cause. Handily a coffee shop is next door. This situation usually means the clientele's behaviour is on the reasonable side. We know where the bar is; however, the press of people is such that it takes us at least half an hour to complete a five-minute walk.

It seems that all of Leiden's population is out on the city's streets. Celebrating *Leids Ontzet*, aka *Drie Oktober*, the date in 1574 when the Spanish siege was lifted during the long and complicated Dutch wars of independence, is a big thing for its population. The sheer quality of the noise envelops us in the autumnal gloaming. The sound made by this party is a real presence. It won't let us go, and insists on accompanying us through its various guises: whether fairground rings, jingles and booms, amplified barkers calling out their maniacal entreaties to the crush of passers-by, the incessant beat of pop music both recorded and live, and that unmistakable diffuse, atonal braying sound that is the mark of thousands of drunken people enjoying themselves. Light flashes and bounces from all manner of places: stages, windows, fairground rides and handheld torches, illuminating gaudily painted stalls, their decorative styles never less than outrageous and often bordering on the satanic, in acid-fried parodies of colour. The smells, too: the overwhelming whiffs of powdered sugar from the candyfloss and huge *oliebollen* stalls (basically deep-fried dough balls for the drunk), fried, raw and smoked fish, with smoked eels doing the biggest trade, Thai and Indonesian stalls with strong spices and rare marinations, the onion tang of a hundred burger stalls and, pervading everything like a benevolent aunt at a christening, that hot, sharp, salt and cardboard smell of chips in a tray.

Leideuuh! My girlfriend and I soak up the scene. It's akin to witnessing a real-life Garden of Delights.

Huge, drunken crocodiles of people edge and stumble towards a monstrously large fairground complex that seems to start near the gigantic windmill, one of the first landmarks as you enter the city centre from the train station. We slowly inch and crunch our way over plastic and glass and foam chip cartons and meet the Affray and Birmingham City, her brother, and his partner, a third Brummie, outside the bar, which is selling beer outside as well as inside. The owner, an easy-going biker lad, is standing behind the portable beer pump on the pavement's edge. We look inside but there is no point going in. A neon-lit, fag-washed and lager-spiked scene is in full progress, one that would have shamed any of Jan Steen's paintings. The owner hands each of us a plastic glass and pours in a mix of alcoholic froth and some liquid, which for this night will have to serve as beer. We chat quickly and move on. There are things to see. Or rather, the crowd moves us on and we surrender to its wider rhythms.

On the evidence of this night, Leideners are a tough and free-speaking bunch of all shapes and sizes, and utterly unashamed as to who they are. Over the last few months I have come to feel this to be my city, despite the high jinks promised by Amsterdam or the easy-going nature of Haarlem. I remind myself again that it's the first place I visited, a few years before moving here. It must be in the stars. This is the 'Stad van Vluchtelingen' (city of refugees), and I'd happily be a new recruit. Leiden, right now, on this whirligig evening in 2000, is very keen to show off its down-to-earth nature. It has a recent memory of being a very poor workers' city: one used to doing its washing in the canals and serving in the many cloth and light-industrial factories that encircled the battered but beautiful old centre. Leiden in spirit reminds me of Lancashire towns such as Bury or Bolton, but with a baked-in and unremovable upper crust courtesy of the many toffish students from the nearby posh-going-on-minor-royal enclaves that surround Den Haag and Haarlem. Still: tonight and tomorrow night, 3 October, belong to those from the squat grey estates that surround the city. De Kooi, Roomburg, Merenwijk, Noord-Hofland. Suspicious-looking lads sporting *petje* and *ketting*, all of whom could be carrying; girls frenziedly chewing gum and walking in an impatient, slightly skittish way. Now and then we see a huddle of dewy-eyed bookish types, doubtless flotsam from the city's famous varsity, representing the large colony of perennial scholars and part-time artists who have also staked a claim here. They and their well-appointed partners revel in the noise but keep a weather eye on an escape route. The *uber*-poshos join in the racket on the margins, sticking close to their fraternity clubs and sorority centres for fear of getting the hiding that they'd normally mete out without consequence themselves. (On those occasions they are usually saved by giving dad's mate in chambers a contrite ring.) We go past one of their bastions. There they are: honking, gelatinous donkeys in ill-fitting suits surreptitiously dropping glasses from the roof. They know coming out on the streets is not the wisest thing to do.

Driven by the press of people, we pass an old corner bar where the clientele seems to be wholly septuagenarian and rolling drunk; the wheezy sentimentalities of the Dutch *levenslieds* that are doubtless deafening inside make only small inroads into the general throb of noise found on the streets. Old fellas hold desperately on to the doorways, their red and white accoutrements, eccentric additions in the city's colours, ranging from scarves to bonnets and rosettes, compete with peeping bellies, scuffed pumps and piss-splattered trousers.

The Birmingham Cities are great company. Engaging and intelligent, they've been travelling too and are back to save up by working the winter season. They represent another gradation of British and Irish travelling type I've come to recognize: the ones who secretly have a plan for sometime in the future but are also happy to join in the madness. This crew are cognizant of the mores of the tribes with which they run, but aware of the time limit they have in the company they find themselves in.

Hours pass without us noticing. It's impossible to escape the crowds. People are absolutely everywhere: scattering and reforming in gangs on the street, crawling down alleyways, falling out of pubs, crying, yelling, looking for a problem or a friend. Drinking beer on the street becomes a mildly obsessive pastime. You never know when you can get to the front of a beer queue to get another one, so you overcompensate and buy three or four beakers at a go. Inevitably this leads to joining the second part of the dance we are currently engaged in: the finding of a public toilet. We decide to stand by the first set of public jakes that we can get easy access to and have done with wandering around. This means we inadvertently end up watching one of the hundreds of cover bands that are playing in the city. The one on the platform opposite us is covering the work of sixties Californian band the Doors. In our drunken state we all decide this really is the Doors, not a bunch of hobbyist musicians from Leiden: for one, they have the sound off pat. Regardless of my beer fug I am struck that, when copying something, the Dutch truly are masters; look at their miniature paintings. I drunkenly reason with myself that this is one of the main, golden strands of Dutch genius: to copy something to a state of sterile perfection, until the life force of the original object or idea doesn't matter, outside of a few well-worn tropes. Then the copyist has the power. Here, surrounded by the smoke of fags, flares and cooking oils, all of which serve to make a hybrid dry ice, the cover band can do no wrong. The gawky keyboardist is the spit of Manzarek and the feral singer pulls off a mighty fine Morrison. They are dedicated to their craft, one that is forever wedded to the mild and boogie tastes of the wider Netherlands public. They even do 'Crystal Ship' and 'Land Ho!' I am genuinely impressed. Their shamanistic nothingness calms us. We are taking it easy, in the nationally approved manner.

Leiden, Tuesday, 3 October 2000. It's past one in the morning. We are now righteously drunk. The Affray fizzes off into the night, yelling and snorting out some mad tale of getting wrecked on a Caribbean island she once worked on. My pals get everywhere, it seems. The bright neon fizz of the street and carnival lights and the undulations of ambient noise frame her tale. In this setting her words may as well be from the Norse Sagas.

We crash where the Affray is staying, a terrace house opposite a soup kitchen. The ambient racket of *Leids Ontzet* follows us into the house. It never really stops. In the early morning the sonorous wail of a brass band wakes me up. I look at my watch: it's barely six o'clock. A procession in the city? At this hour? I have to go to work in any case. My girlfriend and I decide to leave, stepping over the others who are splayed out on the floor. They've had a bottle of wine and the odd funny cigarette as part of a late family catch-up. Although it's much quieter outside there are odd pockets of concentrated noise that suggest things are starting up again. One comes from a procession led by official-looking men, maybe city elders, formally dressed in top hats and tailcoats. There's a marching band accompanying them. Sleep-deprived and rough from the night before, we try not to compute what is going on, preferring to get to the station and catch a bus to the village, and then get some breakfast before cycling to work.

On this gloomy morning Leiden looks like a huge rubbish tip. Small, unsteady-looking cleaning cars scurry round, sucking up piles of cartons, plastic beakers, glass, paper and food waste. Rats scuttle between the mounds. Those still on the street look like they've survived a gas attack in the Great War, walking unsteadily, holding on to a mate for guidance. Nearing the station, on a side street near the De Gulzige Geus, we see a strange movement emanating from under a huge pile of plastic cups and cardboard boxes which slowly erupts and disintegrates. A man cautiously emerges. Pulling himself together, he looks around, attempts to dust himself down and walks on back into the city.

*

Tuesday afternoon. I have a crushing head.

The day has become an odyssey of walking around a designated space of concrete and glass and steel. Now I know what bears feel like in the zoo. But, unlike bears in the zoo, openly standing around looking bored is a no-no. And I'm not sure bears, despite the popular saying, have experienced a beer hangover.

To deal with it as best I can, I have spent the last two hours hiding in a cell trying not to feel sick. This one has *gaasbakken* stacked to the ceiling with tulip bulbs that will be sent out to Italy in November. It's one of the very few cells with anything in it, and therefore one of the few places you can hide in. There are three drawbacks to hanging out here. Firstly it's relatively cool, as the tulips are kept in a state of hibernation by the low temperature. Secondly it's important to look busy in case anyone asks what's going on. I get a hand-operated lift designed for these kinds of stacks. I can get bulbs down and check them, and make sure they are not sickening. That gives me enough of a defence: just stand behind the lift and stare at a tray of bulbs I've lowered down, with the cell door open. See? I'm working. But worst of all is standing amongst the towering stacks of bulbs for hours on end. Being surrounded on all sides by these creaking wooden edifices, each tray weighing five kilograms or so, with some stacks reaching up to the cell roof, is an incredibly unnerving experience. What if one topples? The lot would slowly come down and I would have to race for the door.

I rope the Devon Girl in for company and lookout. We lurk, both sentinels and skivers, playing out an insane parody of work. We count the same bulbs five times, just to pass the minutes. Even with someone as funny as the Devon Girl for company, there's no escaping the existential ennui of having nothing to actually do in a factory, especially with a hangover. Torpor threatens to take hold. Maybe I should move that mini pallet five centimetres to the left, it's not straight. The stack of tulip bulbs it holds is well over ten feet high, but I take a deep breath and, using the lift, slowly nudge the pallet into the desired place. The tower of *gaasbakken* sways and creaks above my head as it slowly finds its equilibrium. I stand by the door, ready to bolt. There. Done. What next?

At the last break I get called to the office. Oh no, I'm getting my papers. Ah, wait: luckily, the fact that I went to the *Drie Oktober* party has let me off the hook with the *schuurbaas*. He likes the fact I have 'taken the time to get acquainted with the local culture and history'. This means work until the end of the week. He's a reserved chap, tall and bespectacled, and one who cultivates a learned air. Not a bad bloke, really. But we, the casual workers, are not really part of his world, nor will we ever be.

*

Wednesday lunchtime, 4 October 2000. Somehow the week has managed to drag itself as far as here. I have spent another unnerving and thoroughly soul-sapping morning 'checking' the bulbs for the Italian orders in the cool cell. This can't go on. After a Cup-a-Soup, the highlight of the day, I join my colleagues and shuffle out for another two-hour session of going through the motions. Giel scuttles over in a state of high excitement. Grinning at me, he waves a set of papers in the air. He tells me we can check the leftover stocks of tulips in the factory. Then we can write down what we find and check the numbers off against the official stock count.

What a dream. We don't have to think about doing nothing until the end of the week. We can sanction our own break times out the back of the factory; indeed, anywhere in the factory. We can pretend to look for lost stock. The relief from not having to think about the rest of the week almost unmans me. Quietly, I shake Giel's hand.

Thursday, 5 October. The Sussex Trawler is one of a big batch of people to go. His forte is standing around looking bored. His very wellbeing seems to depend on it. He's given his papers, which he takes uncomprehendingly. His mate the Dietician gets his marching orders on the same day. No point sacking one and not the other. They both still come in at six o'clock on the Friday for beer and *borrelhapjes*, a tradition that momentarily brings the office staff, the Dutch lads and us scruffs together in some form of comradely unison, even if we still sit at separate tables. At these affairs, the dodgy accountant opens up about his inexplicable love of the Reliant car factory, and the lads in sales, now free from traversing Europe flogging the company's wares, indulge in breezy banter with us. It's normally about football and what naughtiness they got up to during their travels. Some of the older fellows come in from the village. No longer employed to check the bulbs, they still miss the gentle chinwags with their old compadres in this drab and functional canteen. Some spark in life is missing for them, even if they obviously get waited on hand and foot in their comfortable and well-ordered homes. One old bloke doesn't know how to open a can of pop, the ring pull obviously being his wife's department. We help him out, and he blushingly thanks us. They're a good bunch all told, just different.

In between alternate, stirrer-fed mouthfuls of Cup-a-Soup and slurps of beer, the Dietician tells us he and the Sussex Trawler are planning a leaving party for tonight, just for themselves, in their room. The rest of us indulge in mild fantasies over what such a party would mean. Spiked Cup-a-Soups?

*

The following week the Dietician has a further surprise for us. He and the Sussex Trawler pop in on Monday lunchtime to tell us what they got up to. The Friday-night party was a roaring success: they played CDs and danced and got drunk together. They also went to Amsterdam for two whole days: a trip that was the justification for the Dietician's time in the Netherlands.

'I bought a bong. Look! A BONG!'

The Dietician has brought it with him. This glass object, bulbous, egregiously tasselled and alien to its surroundings, suggestively squats on the canteen table.

'Very nice.'

'It's for my mother, so she can have a memory of what I've been up to.'

Break over, we go back into action. I'm cleaning up the crates at the back of the factory, dodging the showers and gusts of autumn weather. A bout of bulb finger is killing me. It's flared up under the nail of my little finger. I've been told this is to be my last week until November.

CITY FUN

IT'S A FRIDAY NIGHT in mid-October and I'm in Leiden with my girl-friend, my end-of-season wages in my pocket. We are in De Gulzige Geus for Lady Hedonist's birthday party, one half of the witty and fun-loving couple from County Louth that the Affray introduced me to. They are rapidly turning into close friends. The Hedonists are the unofficial ringleaders of a group of new acquaintances from seemingly all over: England, Scotland, New Zealand, Ireland, Portugal, Italy and France. A few things unite this disparate body: one is that everyone lives in Leiden or thereabouts. There's also a shared love of having fun, especially in the form of the wild fancy-dress parties that take place at the Hedonists' house, an old worker's terrace just outside the city centre. The place often serves as an overnight stopover for those who missed the last bus to the coast or were too out of it to start up their *brummer* moped the night before.

Lady H is regaling us all about her time as a waiter in a New York bar.

'If a customer didn't tip us we'd spit in their drinks the next time they came in and mix it up. Some bartenders would add drips of their own piss.'

The Hedonists are just back from a long trip to Malaysia, and the Hedonist, a stocky lad whose tough, inscrutable front hides a kind soul, tells us of negotiating rope bridges in the jungles and avoiding the idiot travelling types.

I dip in and out of the conversation, which, like that in any bar, reflects its patrons. Given we are surrounded by a crew of backpackers, travellers and bulb workers who are no strangers to the odder sides of life, the talk bounces around the outer edges of what normal upright Dutch and British society would deem appropriate. The atmosphere is jolly, sharp and a wee bit competitive. Various emotional substrata underpin chatter that ranges from utterly mundane 'bulb talk' to personal idiocies carried out around the world. The two main unspoken subjects are how to negotiate a constantly uncertain future and glorifying wildnesses past.

'I got on the wrong plane at Delhi, I nearly went to Saudi Arabia, I was so messed up on coke I didn't know where I was.'

'These boots I got for work, they're supposed to be "everything-proof", that's why I bought them. But I dropped butter on them and I can't get the fucking stain out, they're not even butter-proof.'

'I was once so high off Thai whisky I lifted up an elephant's tail and kissed its arse in a religious parade.'

'Once I've done this season I'm off to Brittany for the winter. The house is still a shell but the roof is going on. I reckon that at some time in the next two years we will be ready.'

'Did you hear about Dave? You know, the older bloke, often used to drink in Lisse. Died of an overdose in Thailand. Didn't wake up, apparently. Smack. Nice guy, but what are you doing smack in your fifties for?'

'I run to Lisse from Leiden everyday. Saves money, keeps me fit, and anyway I'm keeping clean during the daytime this winter. Drugs in the winter season fuck your mind up.'

'The best place to do acid is in the dunes, it's so peaceful there on a sunny day, just you and nature and nobody else.'

'Anyway the lazy bastard made a bed for himself up in the factory scaffolding. He's even got a mattress and pillows up there. No one's clocked it! He goes there every break.'

'Erm, you got ten guilders handy? I just have to go and get something from this shop ... Just ten, that's all I need. No mate, you don't get it, it can't wait until tomorrow, ah never mind, I'll ask someone else ...'

The music goes up a notch. Dead Kennedys.

This music is our kind of music, that's why we like it here. Part of the fun in the Geus is getting your requests played by the owner, who's also a fan of what we like. The back wall has hundreds of CDs to choose from, with lots of goth, punk and rockabilly, and modern variants of these, or 'approved' contemporary bands like Primal Scream. Another main attraction is a *tostie* made from half a round of Turkish white bread, replete with gherkins, tomato sauce and mayonnaise. The Geus is the only bar we know of that uses these sweet and oily breads for making this premier Dutch snack. One of these is going to be my only food on this long night. I fight off a few hands that aren't looking to pay for their own.

Munching my *tostie* by the bar, I stare at the rock posters on the ceiling, the gleaming rows of glasses hung from the bar top and the bits of bikes and surfboards mounted on the brownish-red walls, and soak up who's in tonight. There are a few Dutchmen and -women near the slot and pinball machines at the end of the bar, under the stairs. Some are punks, including a couple of big lads with shaven heads. A number of local goths pop in, in full regalia. One, wafer thin, wears wraparound shades and leans against the slot machine in the corner, seemingly oblivious to everyone. A faint smile plays around his lips. To his left, fraternity clubs and sorority centres at the machine, is an older bearded gentleman in a grey jumper, utterly unremarkable in every aspect and looking completely out of place. He plays this machine all evening, pausing only to get small change from the bar.

I look round and see a couple of older Brits familiar to me: ones who act as social ferrymen between the Dutch and the rest by virtue, it seems, of living in the city for a long time. These older lads are in their late forties and early fifties. They have evidently been through a lot in their time and don't need to hear the kinds of group confirmations many of the twenty- and thirty-somethings do. One fellow is a familiar figure in town. Dark and sharp-featured, he often wears a wide-brimmed hat pushed down over a long, flowing mane of hair. Cowboy boots, tasselled suede coats and a big hip belt with an enormous metal buckle are other sartorial staples. He stalks his way into bars, a slight figure with a bow-legged walk. Giving off an air of detached cool, his line in patter is straight out of the 1960s. Words like 'cats', 'chicks', 'heavy', 'far out', 'psyched' and 'man' pepper his sentences.

A second is a longhair Geordie biker who belongs to a local chapter. Normally in full leathers, something that complements his outwardly gruff demeanour, he's nevertheless an engaging enough soul who plays in a band or two in town. His party piece is to tell us about when he was doing time and Fred West was brought into the prison.

'We all had to face the wall and shut the fuck up. No one was meant to see where he was going.'

My reverie is interrupted by the Sussex Trawler and the Dietician, who have just turned up. They have spent the day in Leiden, or rather in some of the coffee shops and bars that allow you to skin up in the afternoon. One was Sam Sam, legendary for its pothead vibes. It's a smoky, simple place where you can have a drink and a toke at one of the round barrel tables and listen to dub reggae and other far-out sounds with a number of other mildly addled punk, hippy and traveller types.

That is, if you can get the barman's attention. The two have been there all afternoon. The Sussex Trawler's eyes seem even more detached from his face than usual. His natural lean is further pronounced. It's a miracle he can stay upright. The Dietician is babbling wildly about Sam Sam's owner, a well-known local figure.

'He just sits there all day behind the bar! He doesn't serve anyone!'

The Affray and Young Sunderland show up too. They seem like they've been having a row about something. Still, everyone's happy to have a laugh. Things start to get slowly out of hand, the way they do when people have their last payslip in their pockets and are either off travelling soon or happy to be back in the country. A perpetual state of being in-between states.

Someone appears in fancy dress: a ten-gallon cowboy hat set off by what looks like a onesie and a purple wig. Another follows them dressed as Elizabeth II to the odd laughing boo from some of the rebel contingent here. The music gets turned up a notch.

A collective, euphoric psychosis begins to overtake the Geus. There is suddenly a lot of singing, mostly rebel songs and punk classics. The Sussex Trawler loses it to a number by the Damned, trying to pick up a table that's nailed to the floor and refusing to give in, even though it's plain that the table is going nowhere and the effort is making him wheeze and splutter. What makes him do this? And why do we egg him on? This futile attempt to move the immovable certainly speaks to our perennial ability to live in the moment. We may have no idea what we are doing in the next weeks, let alone months, outside of signing on at some point, but our lives can wait. The lack of seriousness, concern about 'careers' or other humdrum personal responsibilities is a guiding light: a sort of rootless, perpetually spontaneous freedom we love to indulge in, even if we perceive something akin to a concrete wall blocking our way.

I detach a snowboard from the wall and slide down the banister rails.

The Hedonist tries out various shows of strength, such as picking large things up with his teeth, or asking various people to stand on his chest.

For a breather I go outside and find the Affray and Young Sunderland having a full-blown row in the middle of the street. The heads in the coffee shop next door watch on in mute, stoned bafflement. The Affray, who is wearing a luminous-orange Afghan-style coat, kicks Young Sunderland onto the pavement. She then goes back into the bar to continue dancing, a vision of perpetual motion.

I start running round and round the block with Young Sunderland, who is clearly on an inner mission to somewhere. Round we run, through the open square that borders the meeting of the Rijn and two canals, round the corner past the row of tough bars and dark side streets, and past a large corner hangout with a gazebo of sorts jutting onto the street called Coffee and Dreams. This place attracts certain clients who cultivate a streetwise air however out of it they get. Ignoring their stoned, third-eye stares, we run back to the street where the Geus is. We do four or five more laps and then go back to the pub. It feels good, pure, childlike.

Somehow, sometime, we find ourselves back at the Hedonists' funky abode. The party continues, with various wigs, drapes, capes and glittery accessories pressed into action. The music is loud, a mix of the latest Primal Scream LP, the Fall, the Prodigy and various forays into goth.

'Because everybody gets/ What everybody wants!'

It's around nine o'clock in the morning and slowly getting light. We wake up to see Young Sunderland, who is still raving in the living room. It's as if he has continued through the night.

189

'Eh, Aah look like Iggy, me!'

Beaming and glassy-eyed, Sunderland is having a dance on his own to a CD by Alien Sex Fiend. He's wearing a silver-and-blue wig, one of the many costume props to be found around this house. He is topless and his skinny body does resemble Iggy Pop's. He's going for the *Raw Power* look, it's clear. He's also yelling the lyrics at top of his lungs.

'And everybody wants/ What everybody gets!'

In a corner the Affray lies splayed on a chair, senseless despite the noise, covered in various scarves and her Afghan coat. How on earth does she sleep through this?

Deranged by the effects of weed and booze and whatever chemical residue remains from his old chemotherapy treatment, the Sussex Trawler has woken up under a pile of coats in the hallway and is giving the Hedonist, who is passing unconcernedly through the living room on his way to the toilet, an earful in his own house.

'Get the fuck out of this house. Who said you could come in? Get the fuck out!'

He then collapses backwards and, finding a joint on the floor near him, lights it, and smokes in a position resembling an upended tortoise.

It's impossible to dislike the Sussex Trawler, however demented his outbursts are. The Hedonist laughs at the sheer cheek of being told to leave his own house. He's clearly used to it. He's been about in his time, and parties like this are an innocent enough part of the weekend agenda.

My girlfriend and I, however, are battered. We decide to escort the Sussex Trawler back to the bus station, as he obviously has no idea where he is and seems to have lost a good deal of control over his limbs. After the weed he's just had and the remnants of a can of beer he's found to wash it all down, he is out of it again.

This is going to be a difficult job. Outside the Hedonists' house he tries to get on someone else's bike, mounting it from behind, an action which buckles the wheel and nearly punctures his groin on the back of the saddle. Walking with him is clearly the safest option, which should also prevent him from wrecking anyone else's property. We take hold of a side of Sussex each and try to propel him forwards in fits and starts. The success of these motions depends on where his feet are at any one time. Often they seem to be flailing around in an indeterminate space just above the ground, not unlike a puppet's. We traipse unsteadily through the city streets, a bug-eyed, sweating, panting, six-legged beast. We pass groups of sober, respectable and well-turned-out Dutch families, smelling of soap and hair gel and freshly pressed clothes: sensible and normal people who are coming into Leiden for the Saturday market.

Passing the Geus, and seemingly aware of the many disapproving eyes trained on our unsteady progress, the Sussex Trawler jerks into action. He wrestles free of us and, running into the road, adopts a standing star-jump position, waiting for the oncoming traffic.

'Run me over! Run me over! Fucking RUN ME OVER!'

This isn't part of the plan. The Saturday shoppers stare at us. Unable to keep upright for long, Sussex stumbles out of the road and falls into a bunch of handy-looking Moroccan lads who have just come out of the twenty-four-hour shop a few doors down. They give him a shove. Sussex pirouettes and falls onto a passing pram, replete with baby.

The girl pushing the pram screams.

'We're so sorry about this, he's really not very well, we are trying to get him to the hospital.'

Luckily the Leidse Universiteit Medische Centrum is just behind the bus stop. Our excuse is believable, and maybe Sussex's utter derangement does look like some form of psychotic illness. Even in his altered state he seems to realize that falling on a baby in a pram is a bit much. He quietly takes both our hands and we get him to the bus stop without further incident. And, thank God, there is the bus going to Noordwijkerhout. We pay for him, though that doesn't stop Sussex trying to tell the driver where he's going. The word 'Noordwijkerhout' is causing him a lot of difficulty.

'Nawdwwhyderaaht.'

'Nor why der hawt.'

'Nor De Why Der Hot.'

'Nordiehot.'

'Nord.'

'Nor Nor Nor.'

'Nothing.'

'I want to go to Nothing.'

We push him towards the back of the bus. A number of elderly ladies stare disapprovingly and 'tsk' at us.

'*Engels. Joh.*'

Then they return to clucking conspiratorially amongst themselves.

Once aboard, Sussex falls into a near coma. At our stop we shake him awake. Again he has no idea where he is. We tell him we are back in the village. Not asking us anything but displaying an acceptance of his fate that wouldn't shame a saint going to their martyrdom, he gets off the bus and wanders unsteadily towards the centre of the village.

WINTER

ZWARTE PIET, BILLY BASS EN BAR EN BOOS

'KIJK! VOORUIT!'

   'O, o, o, ja! Lekker!'

   'O, wat lekker, mensen!'

   'Drie warrrrme lekkerbekkies voor een tientje!'

Me and my girlfriend are worming our way through a press of people where Leiden's Saturday market, set around the canalized section of the river Rijn, is in full swing. The smells of hot fried fish slug it out with those of roasted nuts and cheese. Leideners like to stroll round their markets and nibble. They are nosey and friendly and prone to swapping jolly little soliloquies with stallholders, what we Brits call a chinwag. They like to browse and compare prices, openly pointing at the differences they find. It's convivial, social and relaxing: a way of showing that, even on a miserable day, they are living the good life. People go extra slow, slower even than in the supermarket. Getting past them is a series of small hells for those used to a faster pace.

The city is extra busy because the Dutch Christmas festival, with its *pakjesavond*, is not far away. This means we can go home early on the evening of 5 December so parents can arrange their children's presents. The prospect of two whole hours free from the factory one afternoon next week, regardless of the reason, is a good thing.

You can buy daft things for *pakjesavond* for your adult mates, too. My girlfriend buys a Billy Bass toy for her brother. Billy Bass is a latex fish mounted on a plaque that wriggles and sings 'Don't Worry, Be Happy' and 'Take Me to the River' when you activate an inbuilt sensor. It's wildly popular: even the lads at work are buying it. I suppose it shows where we are all 'at' in this winter of 2000. The phenomenon fits in seamlessly with other current Dutch mainstream mores, such as digging Robbie Williams or talking about Máxima, the new Argentinian girlfriend of the Dutch Crown Prince, Willem-Alexander. But there again, Dutchmen have a deep interest in most things to do with fish and fishing, especially fishing for carp. A fair number of my workmates spend entire weekends sitting on a wet canal side or pond bank, snuggled in a one-person tent with a flask of something or other and a transistor radio to hand. It's where they seem to commune with a higher power. They can't explain why this is so important, but fishing is an almost spiritual thing for some of them. The carp are talked about like old friends, entities they catch and say 'hello' to, then release in the hope of another meeting a few months down the line.

Amongst the jostle of the market and the main shopping streets, I see something I'm not expecting. Pairs of adults, dressed in bright, synthetic parodies of sixteenth-century costumes, walk through the crowds or hang around shop doorways, greeting everyone while handing out sweets. What makes them stand out is that their faces and hands are daubed completely black.

'What the hell is this?' For someone my age, the act of blacking up is the stuff of 1970s British television, disgraced and long-rejected. A contemptible ignorance. But here it is, in front of me. Apparently this character is called Zwarte Piet. I get the spiel from my girlfriend. He's the workmate of Sinterklaas, and kids really believe it. Sinterklaas, or Sint Nicholas if you're being historical, comes on a steamboat from Spain to the Netherlands bringing presents for the good kids. If you're not a good kid all year round, Piet throws you in his sack and you get taken back to Spain to work in his factory. And you can't lie, because another blacked-up character called Luister Piet has been listening down the chimney all year to check if you've been a good kid. And if you're bad you won't get any nice things and you're going to Spain in a sack. That's the legend. Great.

After a while I notice the shopping streets have Piets at every turn: small Piet dolls are in windows, on gift wrappers, on stickers, replete with curly hair, red lips and an earring. No one bats an eyelid. It's tradition, apparently, and tradition for many here, as I look around at the smiling faces, seems to make it all right. But seeing it en masse in real time is beyond surreal for me. My initial feelings are more of an incredulity that very quickly sours into a weary revulsion: that such a tradition, even if it's supposed to be jolly, 'not racist at all' and aimed at children, is still going on.

There's not much love for such traditions where we're going, though. A few streets away, just behind the massive Hooglandse Kerk, is a bastion of all things not Robbie Williams, Máxima, Zwarte Piet and Billy Bass. We are off to a place called Bar en Boos. Bar en Boos backs onto the Vrijplaats Koppenhinksteeg, which has been in the city for thirty years or so and is a long-standing squat. Like other, similar organizations scattered about Leiden, it puts on gigs, has benefits, hosts numerous alternative activities and is full of all sorts of wild and interesting, sometimes annoying people. We are going because a few pals will probably be there, taking advantage of the vegan meals that get served up in the community kitchen.

We go down a side street to the main entrance just off a very posh street, doubtless to the chagrin of the neighbours, and walk through a large open door. Negotiating a back passageway of sorts with a small stair ramp, we enter another room with a number of tables where people are eating. It's a busy scene, mildly hippy in character, populated by wiped-out ravers, quiet families, well-meaning types in washed-out chain-store clothes and committed-looking streetfighters with their standard uniform of black or dun woollens, combat trousers, big boots and a cap. Hanging on the wall and setting the scene off to appropriate effect is a large drawing of Marinus van der Lubbe, the guy from Leiden who supposedly burned down the Reichstag in 1933.

We see a few people we know. They're busy eating but they're going to Sam Sam afterwards, and they may come back to the Bar en Boos for a drink tonight. There's some kind of band or disco on most weekends. Sometimes a drum circle hosts an open 'bring your own drums' communal bash. I want to go to the drum circle, not because I want to bash along, I just want to see it. So coming back here later sounds like a plan. A volunteer asks us: 'Why not eat here?'

The grub is vegan with Turkish bread and salads. It looks great and professionally cooked, certainly not the home-cooked prison slops I've previously seen my workmates eat. But the pub is still high on my agenda. I get lightly ticked off by a Scottish girl who I worked with back in spring. She's back after a trek in the Himalayas and looks like she hasn't eaten for weeks, maybe in an attempt to model for Egon Schiele. Her dreadlocks are longer than ever, almost touching the ground.

'Do you know how hard it is to get decent vegan food? No, you wouldn't, you cannibal!'

I can imagine that if you profess veganism or vegetarianism as a central tenet of your character, it must be difficult to eat a balanced, chip-free diet on the go in the Netherlands. But there must be places, surely.

'Yeah, there is one place on the Haarlemmerstraat that does vegan food, that one called Moaz. It's good. It's a fucking snackbar, but at least you can get a salad without any fucking meat in it!'

Ah yes, salads with meat, I know of that. Some words lose something in translation: the word 'salad' is not a fail-safe when ordering as there are plenty of varieties that have meat lurking in them, and sometimes what should be a green salad can be served with a slice of ham on top. The best bets are getting a takeaway from an Indian, Thai or Chinese restaurant, but in the last of these a vegetarian meal can be bought with nasi rice, which normally has small cubes of pork in it, something a number of people I know have been caught out by in the past. It's a tricky world, sticking to veganism in Zuid Holland, where milk and cheese are seen as essential pillars of your diet. *Caveat emptor* and all that. We consider eating once more. The water in the communal washing-up bowl looks like the surface of a dockland canal. Let's start with a beer. We trudge over town to Sam Sam.

Down the dingy but weirdly restful Sam Sam alleyway we go, with its collection of tumbledown student houses, murky bricolage shops, a hairdressing salon and a very popular Chinese restaurant. At the end of the street, and giving off a soft light in the gloaming of this winter afternoon, the coffee shop is doing a roaring trade. It's a beautiful place with tall windows, full of out-of-control plants along with hippies, street types and the inevitable washed-up Brit, buying weed or rocking slowly on their haunches while playing board games to reggae.

A few doors up, Sam Sam is its usual stoned-immaculate self. Pushing through the worn double doors, the fug of smoke almost reaches out a hand to welcome you in. The music buzzes away in the corner, and an assortment of stoner and punk types idly chat or slump on barstools while rolling ginormous joints on the counter. We take up a position at the bar because we know it's the best way to get served. Otherwise the owner, after the initial greeting, will forget you're here and carry on chatting up his much younger pretty-boy helper. For him, it seems, we blend in with the surroundings. This is why I always buy two bottles of Hertog Jan to begin with, in case he doesn't register who is shouting for a beer later. Sometimes he will get angry and set his dog, a sort of miniature Yorkshire terrier, on you. The dog will snap round your heels until it gets bored. After that display all is well again.

Sam Sam is a bar where you drift through the afternoon. I love its undercover naughtiness and gentle nature. Everyone, at least those who don't get a bit psychotic from the fumes now and again, is pretty friendly. The music is normally on-the-one. Like every other visit, I end up staring at a large ceramic polar-bear sculpture on a shelf behind the bar, advertising some long-vanished type of whisky. The twinkle of the bar lights and fuzz of the street lighting that make it through the dirty windows sometimes rest on its glazed form, giving it an air of mystery and importance. I really want that polar bear, in its luminescent, chipped, stained majesty. Imagine the years of mild debauchery and stoic ennui it has presided over in here, this antechamber to oblivion.

Oblivion is on hold, though, as the Hedonists and a few of the Bar en Boos crowd enter. They are all going back to the Bar en Boos: something to do on a Saturday night. The city's main club, the LVC, would be another option but it's mostly student discos on a weekend, not really our scene.

We work our way through what must be a crate of bottles. Something about warm smoky bars makes you drink more. I'm mildly out of it, and things are getting bawdy. The huge mirror that takes up most of one wall reflects back on us and makes the place look palatial, like there are hundreds of people just like us in some huge, drained and abandoned swimming pool. The best way to keep afloat is to splash your face with water in the tiny washing bowl in the cramped toilet, a space that wasn't really built for relieving yourself. The unrest room. I splash my face over and over. Time for action. We all stagger out.

In contrast to the busy press of the day, the scene at the Bar en Boos is gloomy and dank. In the air is the unappetizing and sulphurous residue of cooked food going cold. The weird paintwork (dark walls, brightly painted beams) and proletarian aspect of the bar (you are meant to lean against it and drink, it seems) don't help the spirits either. The bloke at the DJ booth cranks out some tunes that are a wee bit too loud for the twenty of us gathered here. The underlying sense of quiet gloom when contrasted with these strident attempts at counter-cultural jollity makes me think of a nineteenth-century workhouse: a place of bangs, clatters, thumps and ultimate disappointments; a place that can tell of battles done with rising damp, rotting wood and burst mains, the Mobiele Eenheid and the neighbours. We are here on a night out. Maybe Sam Sam's atmosphere has unmanned me.

For no particular reason that I can discern, I am cornered by a German punk who is here to see some other German punks on a German punk tour of Dutch squats. Unfortunately, these German punks are now playing somewhere else. He somehow got left behind by the others, so decided to make a night of it here. That's the story. Like many German punks, he is drinking an enormous amount of beer and talks incessantly about German punk and the best methods of fighting the German police. He has a green mohawk and professes a great love for the film *Gremlins*.

I turn to see Lady Hedonist, always one to lift the spirits by doing something daft, dancing alone to Pat Benatar's 'Love Is a Battlefield'. A strange number to play in a place committed to overthrowing the state of things. There again it's a weirdly enjoyable number, breathy goth froth sung to a wall-length mirror, and a number that maybe shows the true invasive nature of mainstream popular music, infiltrating places where it is officially frowned upon. I join Lady Hedonist, aware that we are now the entertainment for everyone else, apart from the German punk and his next victim. We enact Pat's emotional wrestlings as best we can. Somehow the parody dance develops into a scenario where I roll myself on the filthy carpet keeping the drum kit steady on the podium where bands play. I feel its grit and residues worm their way into my skin.

Early the following week, I spend two days in bed with a heavy cold, feeling I have seen enough.

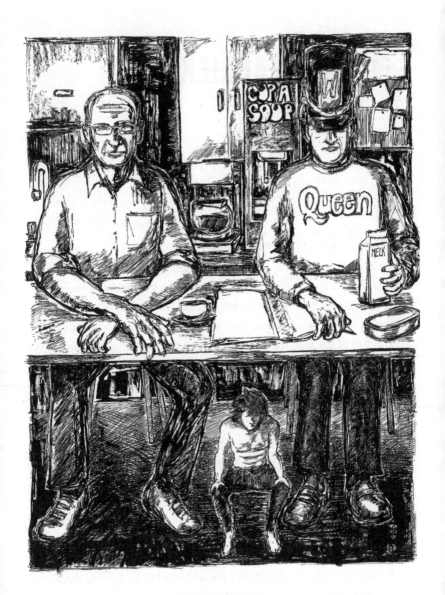

GEZELLIGHEID

MACHINEFABRIEK

A FRIDAY IN EARLY DECEMBER 2000. Standing atop a Hachmang bulb-packing machine, I look out over the gloomy back end of the factory. The machine is a large metal one with a control panel on the front that regulates how bulbs are packed. There are many considerations to take into account, such as the speed a plastic bag is made, the size of the bag, the pressure needed for the staple mechanism that affixes a picture card to the bag, and a number of other prerequisites. Painted a creamy off-white and scoured and scuffed with years of work, multiple breakdowns and quick fixes, this juddering, clattering contraption has something of a Heath Robinson drawing about it. It has a raised platform that hosts a revolving metal wheel with bulb-sized slots, with a wood and metal platform next to it. This is my workstation. At this precise moment I am surrounded by black-plastic crates packed full of lilies: large but delicate bulbs that are sometimes the size of cricket balls. I empty the loose bulbs on the table and then pick them up again, one by one, in a rhythmic motion, pushing them into the holes in the revolving wheel. Given the fact we are currently packing lilies, I add a handful of sawdust to absorb moisture and prevent damage. Overall the job is mildly hypnotic and very noisy. It's also filthy. Some of us wear masks to stop our nostrils turning into dried-out riverbeds of silt, sand, soil, woodchips and other nameless factory muck.

In other corners stand tall wooden stacks of *gaasbakken* full of dahlias. These tuberous bulbs come in all shapes and sizes, and are often covered in the still-wet sand or soil of the field they were grown in. Racks of bulbs are drying out with the aid of some huge standing fans. The drying process means the hall is impregnated with a tangy smell I associate with wet earth. The feeling of gloom created by this concentration of acrid, brown, damp wooden stacks is considerable.

Still, at least I'm back in the factory, on familiar ground. Before this I worked in a medical-supplies place in a light-industrial estate near Hillegom for a little over a week. Here I had to wear personal protective clothing to ensure I didn't contaminate the equipment: a light-blue zip-up suit, white shoe covers and a white hair cap all combined to make me look like a six-foot-something version of Andy Pandy. My job was to watch a machine in a sealed-off room with no external windows make parts for catheters. This work was on a rota of shifts: three days from two o'clock in the afternoon until ten at night, then three days on the overnight shift, then a run of three normal nine-to-five days. Enough to drive you barmy.

On my first day I met a regular: a Vietnamese fellow in his late forties or early fifties who was given to some mildly alarming patter. He would normally run through an energetic little hop from one leg to the other before addressing me with a maniacal grin.

'I fought with the Yanks. We killed the Commie gooks. Yeah. I know how to creep up on you and kill you without you knowing.'

Charming. But he was friendly enough. Other colleagues were also prone to outbursts. When asked what I liked one break time, I was told by a serious-looking French girl to never, ever talk about history again.

'History is finished, you understand? There is none now, why talk about the past with its filthy wars and violence?'

The floor boss, a harassed and decent young man, often allowed break times to overrun, aware that standing by a sealed-off machine just checking that nothing breaks down, for hours on end and in the middle of the night, might send you a little off-kilter. After all that, the cycles back to my girlfriend's parents' house were long, wet, dark and normally in the face of a coastal wind. The night shifts were spent listening to Death in Vegas's long-player *Dead Elvis*. Its air of widescreen dread perfectly fit the grey wet afternoons while I prepared for work.

On one of these afternoons, the radio informed me that George Bush had won the race for president of the United States. The French girl should take note: history is still gasping along. My girlfriend's father shuffled into the bedroom and gesticulated with a half-comical, half-irritated shrug.

'Bush: not good. I don't like this.'

Nope. But like many things in my life, I can't do much about it. And all things considered, I'm glad to be back in the bulb factory; the bulb gloom is Dame Nature's gloom, albeit in part. And I'm in a pleasant enough trance, working to the clanging metallic rhythm of the machine. A crunk and a tsssh, a croak and a thud, and another sealed plastic bag containing two lilies and some sawdust plops onto the short conveyor belt. A picture card showing the variety in full bloom is stapled to the front of the bag, a rare spot of vibrancy in this tube-lit yellow, brown and grey world. It makes a ponderous progress towards a revolving round table, painted sky blue in some random moment of idiocy, where my sluggish workmates pick it up and put it in an oblong cardboard container that can hold twelve such bags. The bags will be slotted together vertically in twos, one bag under another, with the card display at the front. Four times two bags can stand in the container, with a row of four slotted bags balanced on top. Once twelve bags are counted off, the container is added to a larger tray designed for retail use, itself holding four of these containers, or forty-eight packets of two bulbs. So far so simple. So simple in fact that, after an hour of this work, it's a miracle no one passes out from boredom. But no one has yet and we've been at it since seven o'clock this morning.

One of my pals, a short girl from the north of England, stands looking out into space, waiting for another bag to make its way up the conveyor belt. She has been sick in the bin just behind the machine: the first thing she did after getting here. Her eyes are glazed. Whatever it is, it's not food poisoning. Her partner is still sitting in a van in the factory car park, spending the dark morning hours staring out of the driver's window.

Given the racket this old machine makes, I can barely hear the radio, which does mean I can avoid at least three of the recommended five daily doses of Christina Aguilera and, best of all by far, sidestep the adenoidal piss sprayed out by unavoidable monsters of rock Red Hot Chili Peppers, whose abominable number 'Californication' seems to be a particular favourite in the country. I will give the track this: no other music ever penned could be so effective in framing the existential hopelessness of staring out over this cavernous, gloomy, filthy repository for millions of freshly dug tubers.

The guy nominally in charge of the machine is a surly fellow and we try to avoid him. He's happy to do as little as possible during the day but will inevitably find fault with whatever we do get done. Obviously bored, and in a repetitive job that usually means working with snotty, wilful teenagers, messed-up travellers and agency lads who act deliberately stupid to avoid being overworked for the pittance they receive, or the new Polish workers who only speak some German, and with no other prospect of ever doing anything else until he retires, he gets his kicks from playing at being the boss.

'These staples are not straight.'

'You need to put less cards in the holder.'

'Use less soil in the bag.'

'Put the trays in a different order.'

'*Godverdomme*, are you stupid?'

Mate, just fuck off, we all think.

It's understandable why he complains but he never does anything else but wind us and himself up. A vicious circle for all concerned. The Affray has already lost her rag with him for his complaints about her not getting the coffee he wanted, a routine at the unofficial nine-o'clock coffee break that can't be tampered with. The Affray brought back a coffee with two sugars: he has coffee with one sugar. Abruptly, the coffee was thrown on the floor, accompanied by a muttered commentary about foreigners who never seem to do things right. The Affray gives him what for.

'You stuck up, boring old racist fuck. What is the matter with you? Are you like this with your wife, your kids? Look at you, you're pathetic, behaving like a baby.'

She was on the verge of tears. Having a row about getting the wrong coffee is such a pointless way to get through a day coloured by filth and noise and boredom. Slowly this has been forgotten and we inch towards the ten-o'clock morning break time, and finally it's properly light outside. It may be cold and damp, but it's light outside. I decide to get a coffee a bit later and eat one of my three sandwiches standing on the grass in front of the factory. I can soak up some sunlight, however weak or cloud-hidden. There is a danger of going dizzy from the lack of real light.

Friends sometimes tell me of their dark bus journeys in and out of Leiden to work. Not many passengers want to sit next to them and those who will do so in a pained way, with one buttock resting on their seat's edge, as if looking to jump up at any minute. This is usually accompanied by a martyred expression and a frozen stare fixed on the bus's front window. But now and again a quick, nervous glance is sent over to check that no outrage is being committed next to them. This is what happens if you smell rancid on the bus going home, caked in the muck and chemical residue of the bulbs after a day's work. Wearing a mix of stained and torn work clothes and hippy, punk or raver attire doesn't create any sort of *entente cordiale*. Neither does the smell of weed or tobacco about one's person.

I've heard talk of being surrounded by open-mouthed, well-appointed children and nervous mothers, bolshy teens who are nevertheless overly careful about their appearance and the inevitable gaggle of clucking older ladies who seem to stalk the land in threes and fours, ostensibly on days out to city centres, all smelling strongly of soap, the *Algemeen Beschaafd* Dutch perfume. The best way to negotiate any social discomfort is to keep your head down and stick your Walkman on. Some take the most intellectual books they own to pose on the bus with, as a silent two fingers to these model citizens.

'I may be covered in the filth of the fields, doing jobs you don't want to do, but I am a thinker with my Philip K. Dick anthology.'

Thinking of these stories reminds me of what I've got. I curse myself for bringing *One Day in the Life of Ivan Denisovich* to work. A ridiculous choice of subject matter.

Standing outside is also better than standing in a twitching queue for a *bakkie*. Queuing for coffee becomes a daily ritual where workmates shuffle from one foot to another, or raise eyebrows, gurn and expel air from their cheeks while passing mildly impatient comments between each other. I can't be arsed with any of that today. I can grab one in a few minutes. Unlike the others I don't feel the need to get a coffee immediately, at all costs. Coffee is a religion here, the machine cup acting as a dispenser of relief and relaxation, a weird moment of transubstantiation where the body revealed to the initiate is one's own. A moment to enjoy one's enjoyment. And all too soon the moment is over. Back we trudge to pack more lilies in trays.

Dinnertime slowly creeps around. From my high vantage point I see two unfamiliar figures in bulky coats slowly and methodically making their way through the rows of *gaasbakken* like a pair of undercover cops. They come into view and I clock who they are. Oh no, the bulb-checking blokes are here. This means they'll be sitting in the canteen. It's not that they're bad lads: they do their job diligently enough, checking that the bulb varieties are what they are supposed to be, that we are not selling cheap knock-offs or the wrong sizes to unsuspecting customers. It's more that these lads are champion bores and the last thing any of us need this week is to be bored in new ways. Walking into the canteen and getting a Cup-a-Soup (traditional Dutch pea soup flavour, the most glutinous variety on offer), I note that one of the checkers is in full flow. A ponderous chap who looks slowly from left to right when he speaks, he's also balding save for a scrubby patch of sandy hair atop a perma-furrowed brow which he constantly tugs at. Right now this patch of hair is getting a quick, affirmatory twirl and pat as he talks about music to no one in particular. The Dutch lads are busy reading their local papers while sipping at their Cup-a-Soups, now and again looking up to grunt in vague assent. I suspect it's just their way of being polite and showing that they're not ignoring the bulb checker, even though they are. Not that there would be any point in taking up conversation, as the way the bulb checker speaks intimates he can't imagine anyone would disagree with anything he says.

'Queen are the best band in the world. No band has been as good as Queen.'

'Freddie Mercury was a real showman, a true frontman. No one could play to a crowd like him.'

'Their gig at Live Aid was the best gig on the day. It's a legendary gig. It's probably one of the best gigs of all time.'

'The Works is my favourite album, but it's really hard to pick one. They are all brilliant. But that Greatest Hits album they made is the best greatest hits album ever made.'

And so the checker goes on, extolling the virtues of each member of Queen, how they could play better than anyone else in the rock scene and how their non-musical talents make them such fascinating people. I try to read more of Ivan Denisovich but soon give up. Reading about the miseries of the Siberian gulags as a break from packing thousands of bulbs in a Dutch bulb factory is not to be recommended.

There must be something else to read in here. I remember one of the sales staff brought in the Sunday Telegraph after being in London on the weekend. A bulky stack of printed paper, it's in the corner with all the subsections. The only bits that have been read are Sport and Finance. I negotiate some other supplement, some kind of modern-living guide, where there is a column about the doings of a pedigree dog in North London and another about where best to buy the latest soft furnishings. It strikes me that the writing style of the latter, despite the lavish sprinkling of doubt-less obligatory mots du jour, could have been lifted directly from A Handful of Dust.

I look over at the others in the fusty canteen and read out some passages about shopping trends in London to the Devon Girl, who can't really grasp any of it. She's been around the globe, through deserts, jungles and mountain ranges. She looks at me, laughs, taps her head and lights another roll-up. These social fusses and fidgets with all the attendant buzzwords are so far removed from our world it's hard to form any kind of response to them, let alone judgement. Someone may as well try to teach us cuneiform. The English girl who was sick in my bin is sitting in a corner with her partner. Slumped, slack, they look at me uncomprehendingly, as if my words haven't made their way over to them yet. It's like they've been tasered. Another English lad sits in a corner. Shaven-headed and pale, and normally pretty surly when not utterly silent, he abruptly stands up and stalks out. He's not at all interested in making friends. Just here to work and, if other colleagues are to be believed, keep away from drugs.

The collective apathy of the canteen and my stories about how things are going down in the likes of Barnes or Hampstead annoy the checker, who, maybe feeling that his Queen stories are not getting the consideration they deserve, angrily starts talking about the state of factories in the area, and how some of them would be shut down if it were up to him. Break is over.

If the stacks full of dirty brown tubers standing by my machine are anything to go by, it looks like the afternoon will be spent packing some freshly dried-out dahlias. These come in a wide variety of shapes and sizes. The ones we are currently packing look like floppy starfish, with long cigar-shaped tubers dangling from a ventral root. Others are like miniature Mills bombs, hard and bulbous. Yet others crumble in your hands, small, mummified testes on a stick. Putting the bulbs in the uniformly round metal aperture without wrecking the bloody things or taking your hand off takes a fair amount of skill. The trick is not to push the tuber too hard or too deep when an empty aperture slides around. Giving yourself a head start is handy too; best done by filling up the holes before you start the machine and ensuring you have enough bulbs lined up to keep it ticking over.

One thing about the dahlia varieties is the names. Some are extraordinary, maybe trying to reflect a flower whose varieties can be big and brash. Unfortunately the vicissitudes of translation from Dutch to English have intervened in a cruel way when it comes to extolling the virtues of particular varieties. There is one called Wig Sensation. Then there is a yellow-and-purple affair called Kids Climax. A few of us raise our eyebrows. Why haven't they changed the name to something less ... well, awful? Is there any point in asking?

Finally, after hours of gently squeezing various forms of dahlia into the machine, it's time to go home to the village along the dark, skiddy cycle paths, shower vigorously like I'm ridding my body of lice after a tour of duty in a Kaiser's War trench, and have dinner with my girlfriend's family. It's a Friday which means we get to eat a family dinner then slump in front of the telly for a while. My girlfriend's father is the cook. Recently retired, he also really enjoys watching very late-night television, mainly sports programmes about the Grand Prix or cycling, and cooking long, multi-course family meals that he fusses over. The grub is Dutch yeoman farmer fare. Tonight we get oxtail soup with some Madeira sherry as a condiment and *stokbrood* (the Dutch French stick) to dip in it. Following the starter we get to serve ourselves from a metal dish piled full of fried *karbonade*, a form of fatty pork cutlet. Boiled potatoes and a large serving bowl of mixed softly steamed vegetables, cauliflower, carrots and peas, accompany the meat. There is gravy too.

For dessert, and after a glass of white wine, we get a glass tumbler of vanilla ice cream, topped with a ruff of whipped cream that noisily erupts from a spray can. The quality of the cream depends on how vigorously the can is shaken. There's an art to it, one I need to master. After all that food there is no point in doing anything, not even going to De Schotse Bar or Van Der Geest. My girlfriend's mother

213

washes up, something I am laughingly banned from doing. Then she takes her place on the sofa to watch current-affairs and showbiz programmes about the British and Dutch royal families, and I am smilingly quizzed about minor British royals, their love lives, their temperaments. Otherwise she reads a small gossip mag called *Ditjes en Datjes*, which is about the British and Dutch royal families and other, mainly American, celebrities and glamorous criminals. Both parents have been very accommodating and considerate to me, a stranger in their home. Still, conversations are painful and embarrassing: akin to walking over a sump- and rubble-strewn wasteland of broken-down pleasantries, monoglot phrases, endlessly repeated words learned out of a dictionary and pointless, banal exhortations to make a joke out of every situation.

One such conversation is brought about with some fanfare. Apparently there is some official mail for me. Me! An Englishman living in a Dutch house! We go through a new version of our rehearsed pleasantries in polite approximations of both languages as I am handed the letter. It's from the Dutch Immigration Office, who inform me they are processing my claim for a long-term residency card. This card will, according to friends who own one, get your benefits claims passed that tiny bit quicker and show the authorities that you've made an effort to fit in. We decide to stay in and grab a bottle of beer from the fridge to celebrate. Amstel. I realize I am entering a new phase, that of the settled seasonal worker in another land.

EPILOGUE

EPILOGUE

DRUM CIRCLE VIOLENCE

'GET OFF ME, YOU FUCKER. You fucking wanker.'

These and other expletives are coming from the two bodies rolling on the floor, locked together in one writhing, pummelling exertion of anger and frustration. Two of my workmates are having a barney on a sunny Sunday afternoon in September, in Bar en Boos, where the weekly drum circle is taking place. Their exertions kick up an awful amount of muck. Millions of dust particles are suspended in the autumn sunlight pouring in from a large back window overlooking the canal. The drum circle carries on bashing its way towards some form of percussive communality; though more hesitantly, maybe, as it's hard to concentrate on your bongo beats when two English ravers are trying to tear lumps out of each other a few feet away.

Our group watches on. Most of us are giggling nervously, apart from one lad, who looks on in a strange, detached way. I suspect he's the cause of this fight. He's a bit weird, a year or two older than us. He likes staring into space and showing off his bronzed profile under what looks like an Austrian army cap worn by the Good Soldier Švejk. From the clipped conversations I've had with him he seems to be someone who has strayed too far into living out the new dawn brought about by the Second Summer of Love. He also seems a bit thick.

'I do my Tarot reading every day and throw the I Ching. It's a good balance.'

'You know what I don't understand? I speak good German, and I thought if I used that in Holland I'd be accepted. You know, get work straight away, get a head start, but it's not like that. I keep getting weird looks.'

'You fucker.'

'You arsehole, you fucking arsehole.'

Taking advantage of the fact that the two wrestlers are rolling in another direction, I go to the bar and pull out a blue ten gulden note to get a round in. Frans Hals stares idly back at me. This money is soon to be replaced by the EU-wide currency, the euro. It's a shame as I like the design of the gulden notes and the fact that loads of old coins are in circulation. I've had some from the reign of Wilhelmina, the revered matriarch and war leader who hasn't been queen for a good half-century. By contrast the design of the euro notes looks really fucking boring. Bridges. Maybe that's the point: enforce a sort of vague spirit of togetherness upon us all. We are all soon to receive packs of euro coins to prepare us for handling the new money. Some of the Dutch lads in the factory are really unhappy about the euro. There is wistful talk of the Dutch state hoarding all their notes and coins somewhere in the dunes in case this project goes tits up. There is other talk of the euro's introduction being nothing more than a good excuse for a stealth tax, whereby the prices are raised 'to adjust' to the new currency.

'How can they? It's swapping one digital currency for another. Why should that mean the costs are carried by us? Who the fuck said that was OK?'

The Dutch obsession with saving the pennies takes on a populist, political hue. Other changes are less planned. Less than a week ago, last Tuesday in fact, the Twin Towers in New York crumpled into a billowing cloud of dust. The reactions were diverse as the news seeped through the factory.

'Have you heard? We're at war. There's an attack.'

The only solid fact was that something dramatic had happened in America. There were some whoops and smiles from some of the Dutch lads, the most unlikely of sources, you would have thought. It turns out they were billeted with American troops on their national service and harbour grudges. By contrast, some of the supposed New Age ravers wanted immediate reprisals against whoever did it. One Swiss girl, the daughter of an important client, and moreover who looks uncannily like Bobby Gillespie, burst into tears at the news. Unlike the legendary Mr Gillespie, she's a quiet and sweet soul, happy to hum away to herself in Swiss-German. She often writes wistful messages to her parents on the sides of the tulip boxes, with hearts and flowers. We suspected her reaction was more to do with a strong aversion to violence of any form.

We cycled home and switched on the TV, which showed a grey furze as if on the blink. Images of rubble and ash. In the week since there has been nothing else to talk about as we sit on the grass munching our sandwiches in the pleasant autumn sun.

'This is bad, let me tell you. This is the beginning of a whole new bad time.'

'Ach, come on, stop being such a bloody hippy. How do you know that? The Yanks will blow the crap out of them and it'll be over in a matter of weeks.'

'Fucking Americans, they had it coming. Always interfering with everyone in the world.'

'By the way, have you seen how many American flags there are round here? What do the Cloggies do, stash flags until they need them?'

It's true, they must stash flags 'just in case'. Countless Stars and Stripes have appeared as if by magic, hanging from all the flagpoles in the area. Nearly every Dutch house has a flagpole and the effect is startling, especially when cycling through the farmland of the Bollenstreek.

The only pain we workers have had to suffer is the fallout on the radio. The jocose Dutch DJs are at a loss at how to react to such an event. It's also clear they have been ordered not to be frivolous, an impossible undertaking for many of the daytime pack. Their voices have dropped into a much deeper range than is sensible or normal, and they look for simple, world-embracing sentimentalities at every turn. This also means a lot of deep inhalations of breath, interspersed with lots of *ja, jas* and the retelling of their personal reactions to 9/11 and those of their circle. It's as if these lads can't deal with a world that doesn't just offer up simple pleasures such as girls and beer and barbecues, 24–7. And we're fucked if we are going to help them out. They should do a proper job, with their hands, like us.

Sadly the collective public enfeeblement of the DJs has been magnified tenfold by the music they play. Scorpions' 'Wind of Change' followed us around like a wailing child in a supermarket. 'American Pie' and 'Piano Man', both plodding and hateful navel-gazing rubbish of the worst kind, were drafted in on a never-ending rota to show us simple working folk what America must be feeling and thinking right now. After two days there was a vote in the canteen. This radio was killing us. It was making us walk slower, pick orders more lethargically and lose our rags in the packing bay. We voted to turn the radio off. Someone brought in a Rolling Stones CD and stuck it through the tannoy. Spirits lifted to the simple beat music of the Cryogenic Five and the orders got packed. We were too busy for world politics.

'You fucking wanker.'

The kick-off at the Bar en Boos is breaking up the communal vibe of the drum circle. Some drummers are clearly upset. Inexorably the warring couple rolls in fits and starts towards the exit. The guy at the door shuffles over. He may be wearing black combat gear and over six feet tall but he's clearly nervous about having to break this up. He's called the police.

'You know we are peaceful here. It's just a nice day with the drums, fighting should go outside.'

The two roll and slide outside and the door is shut on them. Shouting ensues in the street. After a while things get back on track. The enthusiastic if unintentional polyrhythms again take hold of the room. Smiles break out. Maybe they've been arrested. Then there is a knock on the door. One of the fighters walks back in.

'I told the coppers to do one, sling their hook! None of their business, it's a domestic!'

We ask where the other is.

'He's on the roof.'

He appears through a window, now that the police have left.

Later we all go to a nice bar in town where the literary types hang out. It's as if nothing ever happened. The world may be changing, but this bunch of rogues have life in them yet.

RICHARD FOSTER is a writer and artist living in the Netherlands.

He is the curator of the Museum of Photocopies.